BIBLE
Crosswords
Collection #11

Compiled and Edited by
Ellyn Sanna

BARBOUR
PUBLISHING, INC.
Uhrichsville, Ohio

Published by Barbour Publishing, Inc., P.O. Box 719, Uhrichsville, Ohio 44683
http://www.barbourbooks.com

 Member of the
Evangelical Christian
Publishers Association

Printed in the United States of America.

BIBLE
Crosswords
Collection #11

ACROSS

1. "But whoso hath this____ good" (1 John 3:17)
6. Ratio of the weight of a given volume of a substance to that of an equal volume of another substance (abbr.)
8. Operatic solo
9. Mother of Hezekiah
12. Kind; sort (pl.)
15. Gorged
17. Tall spar
18. Time frame? (abbr.)
19. O.T. bk.
20. Crush
22. Angered
27. Frequent follower of what or as
28. Good buy (colloq.)
29. Great Commission verb
30. Relative of corp.
31. Teacher
32. Near
33. Capital of Moab
34. Father of Heber (Luke 3:35)
35. Cried
37. Pile
39. "And he [Josiah] defiled ____ " (2 Kings 23:10)
42. Absalom rode one
45. ____ down
46. "False teachers...who...bring in ____ heresies" (2 Peter 2:1)
49. Noxious weed
52. Outside; outer (prefix)
53. Those not included in the clergy
55. Conjunction
56. Benign skin tumor
57. Greek letter
58. Engineering field (abbr.)

DOWN

1. "Before Abraham____, I am" (John 8:58)
2. Mouth (pl.)
3. Traditions
4. Father-in-law of Michal (1 Samuel 25:44)
5. What Lot did in the gate of Sodom
6. "____ called Zelotes" (Luke 6:15)
7. Mirror
10. Chem. symbol
11. Part of the psyche
13. Midwest state (abbr.)
14. State or Main (abbr.)
16. Preposition
19. Father of Mary's husband (Luke 3)
20. Minor prophet
21. Prior to this (arch.)
22. Type style (abbr.)
23. Father of Solomon's adversary (1 Kings 11:26)
24. Thing to hail
25. Land of Moses' birth
26. Kind of doctor (abbr.)
28. Spanish matron (abbr.)
32. One of the sons of Zophah (1 Chronicles 7:37)
34. "And all the women...brought that which they had ____ " (Exodus 35:25)
35. Reporter's question
36. Chem. symbol
38. "I will not give thee of the land of the children of ____ " (Deuteronomy 2:19)
40. Is in debt (arch.)
41. Favorite school subject, for some (abbr.)

Crossword

Grid (with entered letters):

- 1. WORLD
- 5. S
- 6. SG
- 8. ARIA
- 9. ...I (9,10,11)
- 12. IL
- 13. KS
- 15. SA ... 16. TED
- 17. MAST
- 18. (18)
- 19. OS
- 20. MASH
- 22. INCENSED (22,23,24,25,26)
- 27. IF
- 28. STEAL
- 29. GO
- 30. CO
- 31. RABBI
- 32. BY
- 33. AR
- 34. SAL
- 35. WEAT (35,36)
- 37. HEAP
- 38. A
- 39. OPH (39,40,41)
- 42. MULE
- 45. WEAR
- 46. DAMNABLE (46,47,48)
- 49. TARE (49,50,51)
- 52. EXO
- 53. LAITY (53,54)
- 55. OR
- 56. WEN
- 57. ALPHA
- 58. EE

43. ____ land
44. Son of Shobal (Genesis 36:23)
46. What washed Nebuchadnezzar in
    the wilderness for seven years
47. Hatchet
48. ____ service
50. Fish eggs
51. Before (poet.)
54. How one pronounces *ja*

by Teri Grottke

ACROSS

1. Son of Benjamin (Genesis 46:21)
4. Ruth's sister-in-law
9. Pronoun
11. Son of Zephaniah (Zechariah 6:14)
12. Wake
13. ____ what?
14. Son of Aram (Genesis 10:23)
15. Where the shewbread was
16. Skin
17. "____ thy cause with thy neighbour himself" (Proverbs 25:9)
19. Made useless
21. Family of exiles (Ezra 2:44)
22. The Great ____
23. More astute
24. Assistant to Ezra (Nehemiah 8:7)
27. Consume
28. Certain muscles, according to your personal trainer
30. Conjunction
31. Parched
34. City in Asher (1 Chronicles 6:75)
37. Grain mentioned in Isaiah 28:25
38. Exhaust
39. Are
40. "Come before his presence with ____ " (Psalm 100:2)
43. Give heed to
47. Esau's father-in-law (Genesis 26:34)
48. Miner's trove
49. Father of Jeroboam (1 Kings 11:26)
51. Solomon's great-grandson (1 Kings 15)
52. U.S. founder of Girl Scouts
53. Grate the teeth
54. Carve

DOWN

1. Second judge of Israel
2. He was given fifteen more years to live
3. Preposition
4. Daniel Webster, for one
5. What kings and sleepyheads wear
6. King of Assyria (1 Chronicles 5:26)
7. "Of the tribe of ____ were sealed twelve thousand" (Revelation 7:6)
8. Pronoun
9. Created
10. Regarded
13. Commandment mountain
15. Bible weed
16. ____ the Bethelite (1 Kings 16:34)
18. Exert or busy
20. Employ
23. Blanket or suit
24. Where Auntie Em lived (abbr.)
25. Also
26. Eight adults lived aboard this
28. Preposition
29. Near
32. Eve was made from one of Adam's
33. To Thomas, this was believing
34. Ancient Hebrew liquid measure
35. "The Pharisees began to ____ him vehemently" (Luke 11:53)
36. "Will the men of ____ deliver me and my men into the hand of Saul?" (1 Samuel 23:12)
38. One of the sons of Japheth (1 Chronicles 1:5)
40. One of the sons of Cush (1 Chronicles 1:9)

41. Probiscus
42. Chew
43. N.T. book (abbr.)
44. Mountain (comb. form)
45. "Behold, I make all things ____"
    (Revelation 21:5)
46. Lair
50. Chemical symbol (abbr.)

by Teri Grottke

ACROSS

1. 66 or 80, for example (abbr.)
4. Father of Ethan (1 Chronicles 6:44)
9. Laughing sound
11. Jether's son (1 Chronicles 7:38)
12. One of two
13. Preserve
14. Compass dir.
15. "Bread corn is bruised;...nor break it with the ____ of his cart" (Isaiah 28:28)
16. Ancient entrance
17. One of the families of the tribe of Benjamin (Numbers 26:39)
19. "They made their lives bitter... and in all ____ of service" (Exodus 1:14)
21. Certain vessels
22. ____ fried
23. Laziness
24. Achieve
27. Poetic contraction
28. April correspondent
30. Together with (prefix)
31. Wife of Joseph (Genesis 41)
34. Possessor
37. Commit larceny
38. Son of Roboam (Matthew 1:7)
39. Note on diatonic scale
40. Reluctant visitor to Saul in Damascus
43. "Surely Moab shall be as Sodom...even the ____ of nettles" (Zephaniah 2:9)
47. Biblical verb, KJV
48. Drum or drop
49. Son of Gad (Genesis 46:16)
51. Bind
52. She may be out to pasture
53. Identifies
54. Occurrence (arch.)

DOWN

1. Measles symptom
2. "For my soul is full of ____" (Psalm 88:3)
3. Apiece (abbr.)
4. Son of Levi (Genesis 46:11)
5. List components
6. Pronoun
7. Ship steering
8. European isle (abbr.)
9. Loathe
10. Unit of measure for manna
13. Father of Melchi (Luke 3:24)
15. "____ meanest thou, O sleeper?" (Jonah 1:6)
16. Tiny winged insect
18. More destitute
20. Likely
23. Red or Dead
24. Simile component
25. "Out of whose womb came the ____? and the hoary frost of heaven" (Job 38:29)
26. Conjunction
28. Pronoun
29. With "factor," a group of antigens
32. Memo
33. Son of Gideoni (Numbers 1:11)
34. Minor prophet (abbr., var.)
35. "Who hath gathered the ____ in his fists?" (Proverbs 30:4)
36. Refuge for David, when first fleeing Saul (1 Samuel 19)
38. Hook
40. City of the tribe of Issachar (1 Chronicles 6:73)
41. Continent
42. Instruction manual word
43. Competition
44. Weather beaten

45. Before (poet.)
46. Gershwin
50. Linking verb

by Teri Grottke

ACROSS

1. "The earth shall ____ before them" (Joel 2:10)
6. Edify
11. Repast
12. Father of "mighty men" (1 Chronicles 11:34)
14. Pronoun
15. Fearful things
17. Look, see! (arch.)
18. Printer's measure
19. Bosc, Anjou, et al.
20. Name of two O.T. books (abbr.)
21. Date approx. 100 yrs. before Babylonian captivity, to Caesar
23. Age of Joshua when he died: one hundred ____
   "Before Abraham ____, I am" (John 8:58)
25. Son of Judah (Genesis 38)
28. "Believe not every ____" (1 John 4:1)
31. "To meet the Lord in the ____" (1 Thessalonians 4:17)
32. Take advantage of
33. Gem in the fourth row of the ephod
36. Son of Pashur (Ezra 10:22)
39. Consumed
40. Owns
42. Article
43. Country part of the British Commonwealth, until 1961 (abbr.)
44. Sponsors
46. Linking verb
47. Conjunction
48. Fullness of this dwells bodily in Jesus
50. Number one?

51. "Doth not even ____ itself teach you" (1 Corinthians 11:14)
53. Son of Chislon (Numbers 34:21)
55. "A ram caught in a thicket by his ____ " (Genesis 22:13)
56. Jobab king of ____ (Joshua 11:1)

DOWN

1. Extinguish
2. "What's ____?"
3. Suitable
4. Part of a castle
5. Maketh a mistake?
6. "Sow not among ____ " (Jeremiah 4:3)
7. "Bringest certain strange things to our ____" (Acts 17:20)
8. Balaam's beast
9. Abbreviation preceding AKC winner
10. Son of Meraioth (Nehemiah 12:15)
11. What a dog often does
13. "Nor eat ____ grapes, or dried" (Numbers 6:3)
16. Feminine name
22. Put an end to
24. "They that are unlearned and unstable ____ " (2 Peter 3:16)
26. Insolent talk
27. Linking verb
29. King of Assyria (2 Kings 15)
30. O.T. book
33. Thessalonian Christian (Acts 17)
34. Wife of Jerahmeel (1 Chronicles 2:26)
35. Island Paul visited on his way to Tyre (Acts 21)
36. "Will he ____ thy riches?" (Job 36:19)

37. One of the children of Anak (Numbers 13:22)
38. His son was one of Solomon's twelve officers (1 Kings 4:10)
41. Residue
44. Symbol of power
45. Father of Heber (Luke 3:35)
48. King Ahaziah was wounded near here (2 Kings 9:27)
49. Accomplished
52. Preposition
54. Word in a command

by Teri Grottke

ACROSS

1. Returning exiles, the children of
   ____ (Ezra 2:44)
6. Standoffish
11. ____ of refuge
12. Mother of Samuel
14. "____ if!"
15. Encountered
17. Biblical pronoun
18. Latin abbr.
19. Made with yeast
23. Take a wrong turn
24. City where Isaac died
   (var., Genesis 35:27)
25. Physicians' group (abbr.)
26. Looked at
27. Greet
28. Gossips
30. Brother of Harnepher
   (1 Chronicles 7:36)
32. On the outside (prefix)
33. Son of Midian (Genesis 25:4)
35. O.T. minor prophet (abbr.)
38. Father of Azareel
   (Nehemiah 11:13)
40. More painful
42. Hearts, for one
43. Offering
46. Preposition
47. Hospital inits.
48. King Og's kingdom
   (Numbers 21)
49. Pronoun
50. Aka Belteshazzar
53. He prophesied bondage for Paul
55. Bear or bee
56. Included in the inheritance of the
   tribe of Asher (Joshua 19:27)

DOWN

1. He was "smote" by Jael
2. Clara Bow, the ____ Girl
3. City near Bethel
4. Part of the hemoglobin molecule
5. Wife of Joseph (Genesis 41)
6. "Say ____"
7. ____ it on
8. Single
9. ____ a roll
10. Prettier
11. City in Assyria (Genesis 10:11)
13. Cattle crowds
16. Arabian city (Isaiah 21)
20. Brother of Joab
   (1 Chronicles 2:16)
21. Assign worth to (arch.)
22. Palm or line
23. "He that hath a bountiful ____
   shall be blessed" (Proverbs 22:9)
26. Son of Zerahiah (Ezra 8:4)
29. Relative of a borough (abbr.)
31. Son of Jether (1 Chronicles 7:38)
33. Alleviated
34. Servant of Gideon (Judges 7:10)
36. Middle Eastern language (abbr.)
37. City in the inheritance of the
   children of Simeon (Joshua 19:4)
39. Southern European country
40. His son Jonathan served in
   David's army
   (1 Chronicles 11:34)
41. Asiatic deer (pl.)
44. Linking verb
45. Comparative conjunction
48. Get-together, for a purpose
51. Favorite first word?
52. Preposition
54. Command word

by Teri Grottke

ACROSS

1. Cake mix maker (last name)
6. Amasses
11. Store under pressure
12. Has (arch.)
14. Conjunction
15. Touched
17. City near Bethel
18. Military abbr.
19. Marian, et al.
20. Chemical element (abbr.)
21. N.T. book (abbr.)
23. Gilded or Jazz
24. Son of Jether (1 Chronicles 7:38)
25. Wipe away (arch.)
28. Ammonite who invaded Jabesh-gilead (1 Samuel 11)
31. More than one orthopedist (abbr.)
32. Normal, but maybe not for Nicklaus
33. "For the ____ shall be prosperous" (Zechariah 8:12)
35. "Smote all their enemies with the ____ of the sword" (Esther 9:5)
38. Familiar cavern sight
40. Exclamation
42. Son of Elishama (1 Chronicles 7:27)
43. I ____ (Jehovah)
44. Struck (arch.)
46. Laughing sound
47. Eastern seaboard state (abbr.)
48. Worn by the disciples, among others
50. Simile word
51. Hackneyed
53. Son of Reuel (Genesis 36:13)
55. ____ days
56. "A sceptre...shall...destroy all the children of ____" (Numbers 24:17)

DOWN

1. Dread
2. Pronoun
3. ____ degree
4. Son of Shem (Genesis 10:22)
5. Family of returning exiles (Ezra 2:35)
6. Grasp (arch.)
7. Some of Bo-Peep's brood?
8. Conjunction
9. Required subject in school (abbr.)
10. Escalator option
11. Room or walk
13. Judah stayed with him in Adullam (Genesis 38)
16. Archaeological site
22. In the course of
24. Brother of Moses
26. Before (poet.)
27. Double this for a deadly fly
29. Likely
30. Laughing sound
34. Condemned
35. Belonging to the evil one
36. Son of Levi (Genesis 46)
37. Son of Seth (1 Chronicles 1:1)
38. Prohibit
39. Wrong
41. Son of Zophah (1 Chronicles 7)
44. Father of Heber (Luke 3:35)
45. King of Israel, son of Baasha (1 Kings 16:8)
48. "Gal" of songdom
49. Pronoun
52. 'Bye, to Brits
54. Preposition

by Teri Grottke

ACROSS

1. Regal
6. "Beeroth of the children of ____" (Deuteronomy 10:6)
11. Pronoun
12. "A workman that ____ not to be ashamed" (2 Timothy 2:15)
14. Dir.
15. Hot ____
17. Old Testament book
19. Medical abbr. for delirious state
20. Tyre and ____
21. Son of Aram (Genesis 10)
23. Yes!
24. Arsenic (abbr.)
26. "As thou goest unto ____ a mount of the east" (Genesis 10:30)
30. Another name for Hagar
34. Son of Midian (Genesis 25:4)
35. ____ wave
36. Jesse's third son (1 Chronicles 2)
38. Name that means "son of my sorrow"
39. Note on diatonic scale
40. "Where his tent had been...between Bethel and ____" (Genesis 13:3)
42. Linking verb
43. O.T. bk.
46. Wheat by-product
50. Ignore
51. Expiates
53. ____ art
54. In nearest proximity
56. Pronoun
58. What to do with rosebuds?
59. Reposed

DOWN

1. Chess piece (abbr.)
2. Possessive pronoun
3. Insect
4. Some tennis serves
5. Biblical pronoun
6. Warrior in David's army (1 Chronicles 12:6)
7. Site of threshing floor where Joseph mourned Jacob (Genesis 50)
8. Son of Abinadab (2 Samuel 6:3)
9. Furniture tree
10. Dir.
13. Basketball pass (colloq.)
16. Masculine nickname
18. Article
21. Biblical verb
22. Son of Eliphaz (1 Chronicles 1:36)
23. Capital of Moab (Numbers 21:15)
24. Naaman preferred this river in Damascus to the Jordan (2 Kings 5)
25. Near where John the Baptist baptized (John 3:23)
27. Greek letter
28. Part of a garment
29. Band or chair
31. Consumed
32. Cotton ____
33. Fuss
37. Sighing sound
38. Grievous
41. King of Judah, et al.
43. Preposition
44. So extreme
45. Competent
47. Tea, for one
48. Picnic pests

49. The royal ____
50. Retreat, for some
52. Pronoun used for a country
53. King of Bashan (Numbers 21)
55. Conjunction
57. "Mr. ____" of TV fame

by Teri Grottke

ACROSS

1. Dignity
6. Solomon's throne had six of these
11. What Benjamin was first named
12. Trusts (arch.)
14. Son of Aram (Genesis 10)
15. Brother of Rephah (1 Chronicles 7:25)
17. City near Bethel
18. O.T. bk. (one of two)
19. Stickers
20. Union Pacific, e.g.
21. Airport code on the Big Island
23. "Of Keros, the children of____" (Nehemiah 7:47)
24. Son of Jether (1 Chronicles 7:38)
25. Baby
28. One of Levites named in the book of the kings (1 Chronicles 9:15)
31. Mountain (comb. form)
32. "They have gone in the way of Cain, and ____ greedily" (Jude 1:11)
33. Became stable
36. Jesus healed his mother-in-law
39. Biblical verb (KJV)
40. Fish eggs
42. O.T. bk.
43. Laughing sound
44. Where Abraham pursued those who had captured Lot (Genesis 14:15)
46. ____ a tee
47. Preposition
48. He accompanied Paul into Asia (Acts 20:4)
50. Pronoun
51. Interior or inner part

53. Among the new generation of Israel (pl., Numbers 26:16)
55. Prepared
56. Amorite king (Joshua 10:3)

DOWN

1. Father of Tabrimon (1 Kings 15:18)
2. Subatomic particle (suffix)
3. Conjunction
4. Column name in multidigit addition
5. Got up (arch.)
6. Son of Judah (Genesis 38:5)
7. A-one
8. N.T. bk.
9. Subject taught by a coach? (abbr.)
10. Comics heroine Brenda, and others
11. Son of Jogli (Numbers 34:22)
13. Adullamite who was Judah's friend (Genesis 38)
16. City near Bethel (var.)
22. "Many knew him, and ran ____ thither" (Mark 6:33)
24. John the Baptist baptized here (John 3)
26. Masculine nickname
27. "But as the days of ____ were" (Matthew 24:37)
29. "Of ____,the family of the Erites" (Numbers 26:16)
30. Strike with force
33. She hid the Hebrew spies
34. Keynote speaker
35. Jesus healed a man with this disease on the Sabbath
36. "There, in a portion of the law-giver, was he ____" (Deuteronomy 33:21)
37. Lying below the earth's surface

38. The _____ of the Fisherman
    (West novel)
41. O.T. minor prophet (abbr., var.)
44. Out or over
45. There's companion
48. Baltic, for example
49. Tease
52. "As _____ forgive our debtors"
    (Matthew 6:12)
54. Note on the diatonic scale

by Teri Grottke

ACROSS

1. The great I ____
3. Stay and chat
8. Article
10. Son of Dishan (Genesis 36:28)
12. Son of Shemaiah
   (1 Chronicles 26:7)
13. Santa's sound
14. "Today shalt thou be with me in
   ____" (Luke 23:43)
16. "____ paint"
17. "I see"
18. Minor prophet (abbr.)
19. Electrical abbr.
21. Linking verb
22. "____ hath good report of all
   men" (3 John 12)
25. Single bill
27. Hence
28. Hospital inits.
29. Continent (abbr.)
31. Brother of Shoham
   (1 Chronicles 24:26)
33. Middle Eastern crop
35. Capital of Moab
36. Exists
38. Chemical symbol for tin (abbr.)
39. Acorn tree
40. Ooze
42. Handles clumsily
44. Grain named in Isaiah 28
46. City near Bethel
47. Commercial spelling of a word
   that means facile
48. Preposition
50. Retirement acct.
51. Returning Jew from exile
   (Nehemiah 7:7)
55. The Holy Spirit wouldn't let
   Paul and Silas go here
58. Manna measure

59. Understanding
60. Masculine nickname

DOWN

1. Son of Ulla (1 Chronicles 7:39)
2. Disfigure
3. Expresses
4. Possessive pronoun
5. Cut off
6. Preposition
7. Electronics giant (abbr.)
8. "Ir, and Hushim, the sons of
   ____" (1 Chronicles 7:12)
9. Memo
10. Away from (prefix)
11. "That at the ____ of Jesus"
   (Philippians 2:10)
15. Unclear
16. Used to be
20. Sky, to Simone
22. Family room
23. Dressed ____ the nines
24. Eastern U.S. university (abbr.)
25. Minor prophet (var., abbr.)
26. Abner's father (1 Samuel 14)
29. What a veteran is
30. Question
32. Slick or skin
33. Atop
34. Promise
37. "Of Keros, the children of ____"
   (Nehemiah 7:47)
38. Dir.
40. Box ____
41. Nation God called against
   Babylon (Jeremiah 51:27)
42. "The Princess and the ____"
   (classic fairytale)
43. "The border shall fetch a compass
   from ____" (Numbers 34:5)
44. It may stick out on Olive Oyl

45. Son of Bela (1 Chronicles 7:7)
49. Christmas tree
52. A city of Judah (Joshua 15:32)
53. Minor prophet (abbr.)
54. Church denomination (abbr.)
56. Masculine pronoun
57. "_____ cannot serve God and mammon" (Matthew 6:24)

PUZZLE 10

by Teri Grottke

ACROSS

1. Shoe parts
6. Greek form of Uzziah
11. Son of Levi (Genesis 46:11)
12. Father of Baruch
    (Jeremiah 32:12)
14. Masculine nickname
15. Son of Adiel (1 Chronicles 9:12)
17. School subj.
18. Vote
19. Father of Darda (1 Kings 4:31)
20. Pronoun
21. Family of returned exiles
    (Ezra 2:57)
23. Pilot makes one
24. ____ change
25. Assign (arch.)
28. They come in flights
31. Slangy denial
32. It gives a hoot
33. Cauterized
36. Address
39. ____ blond
40. Construction necessity (abbr.)
42. Jane ____
43. Phonetic sound
44. Exhibits
46. Hospital inits.
47. "The kingdom of heaven is ____
    hand" (Matthew 3:2)
48. Son of Elioenai
    (1 Chronicles 3:24)
50. Biblical exclamation
51. Catch one's eye
53. Glided
55. What Simeon was called at
    Antioch (Acts 13:1)
56. "The heifer...which is neither
    ____ nor sown"
    (Deuteronomy 21:4)

DOWN

1. Greek form of Sodom
2. Buckeye state (abbr.)
3. O.T. bk.
4. "He [Samson]...dwelt in the top
   of the rock ____" (Judges 15:8)
5. Son of Jahdai
   (1 Chronicles 2:47)
6. What the Israelites missed in the
   wilderness
7. Ardor
8. Son of Bela (1 Chronicles 7:7)
9. City near Bethel
10. "Pass ye away, thou inhabitant of
    ____" (Micah 1:11)
11. Early descendant of Adam
    (1 Chronicles 1:2)
13. What a good dog does
16. Pronoun for a seafaring vessel
22. Son of Asher (1 Chronicles 7:30)
24. Bribed
26. Wax or wig
27. Article
29. Big ____
30. Reverence
33. Antichrist
34. Son of Mehir
    (1 Chronicles 4:11)
35. Merchant
36. Contention
37. Became aloof
38. "When ____...had heard these
    things, he was troubled"
    (Matthew 2:3)
41. "Of Keros, the children of ____"
    (Nehemiah 7:47)
44. Visage
45. Father of Heber (Luke 3:35)
48. Verb for flower child
49. Mount where Aaron died
    (Numbers 20)

52. Polynesian woody plant
54. I (pl.)

by Teri Grottke

ACROSS

1. Stop! (arch.)
3. Son of Tahath
   (1 Chronicles 6:24)
8. Father of Simon Peter
10. Assyrian god, which had a house in Nineveh (2 Kings 19)
13. Jealous gems?
15. Nephew of Abraham
17. Pronoun
18. Linking verb
19. Home of the brave (abbr.)
21. Postember state
22. Reproved
25. "In the night ____ of Moab is laid waste" (Isaiah 15:1)
27. Dir.
28. Where Miami University is (abbr.)
29. Hectare (abbr.)
31. Of starch (comb. form)
33. Pilfers (colloq.)
35. Musical abbr.
36. Where "The Music Man" was set (abbr.)
38. Figure on many TV crime shows (abbr.)
39. Hardwood
40. Son of Joktan (Genesis 10:26)
42. Son of Salah (Genesis 10:24)
44. Exclamation
46. Metric abbr.
47. Part of middle-school curriculum (abbr.)
48. Word in a command
50. Big ____, CA
51. Age of Jehoiachin when he began his reign
55. Deception
58. Too
59. Commanded
60. Strike

DOWN

1. Domicile
2. Chemical suffix
3. Except that
4. To free, with "of "
5. Assign
6. Hesitation sound
7. Biblical exclamation
8. "He is a ____, which is one inwardly" (Romans 2:29)
9. Son of Ulla (1 Chronicles 7:39)
11. Attired
12. O.T. minor prophet (abbr.)
14. First name of famed football coach
16. Symbol of thorium
20. "As ____ in summer...so honour is not seemly" (Proverbs 26:1)
22. ____, the Beloved Country (Paton book)
23. Preposition
24. Son of Benjamin (Genesis 46:21)
25. Eleventh letter of the Hebrew alphabet
26. Mischievous child
29. Was told, KJV style
30. Question
32. Untruth
33. Where Durban is (abbr.)
34. Nineteenth-century American writer
37. Prepare for battle
38. AL lineup abbr.
40. Assyrian king mentioned in Hosea
41. Alter
42. N.T. epistle (abbr.)
43. City where David took "exceeding much brass" (2 Samuel 8)
44. Snake

45. With Aaron, he held up Moses' arms
49. City built by descendants of Benjamin (1 Chronicles 8:12)
52. To cause to be (suffix, Brit.)
53. Bk. of the Torah
54. Father of Hophni
56. Note of the diatonic scale
57. Singer Ames

PUZZLE 12

by Janet W. Adkins

ACROSS

1. Priestly garments
5. "Except your righteousness shall ____ the righteousness of the scribes" (Matthew 5:20)
7. Linking verb
8. Replied
10. "Give unto the Lord the glory ____ unto his name" (Psalm 29:2)
11. "Can a maid forget her ornaments, or a bride her ____?" (Jeremiah 2:32)
1☐. Of flying (comb. form)
14. Son of Seth
15. "Israel did ____ manna forty years" (Exodus 16:35)
17. "Yea, the ____ hath found an house" (Psalm 84:3)
19. "Employer" of Hagar
21. Oft-used abbr.
22. One (Ger.)
23. Rate of speed (abbr.)
24. Where Montauk is (abbr.)
25. "All they that cast ____ into the brooks shall lament" (Isaiah 19:8)
27. "They ____ in thee, and were not confounded" (Psalm 22:5)
29. "Agnus ___"
30. Pay attention
31. "Yet will I bring ____ plague more upon Pharaoh" (Exodus 11:1)
32. "____ ye, and believe the gospel" (Mark 1:15)
34. "And Nathan said to David, Thou ____ the man" (2 Samuel 12:7)
35. End or line
36. John, to a Scot

37. "He made a ____ about the altar" (1 Kings 18:32)
39. "He shall be like a ____ planted by the rivers" (Psalm 1:3)

DOWN

1. Chopping tool
2. Public national library (abbr.)
3. "Upon these we ____ more abundant honour" (1 Corinthians 12:23)
4. "He hath put down the mighty from their ____" (Luke 1:52)
5. Before (poet.)
6. 502, according to Cicero
7. Charismatic atmosphere
9. God spoke in Bible times through these
10. Rely
11. Immediately (arch.)
12. Serving of corn
13. "All they which dwelt in ____ heard the word of the Lord Jesus" (Acts 19:10)
14. Great Lake
16. "I was afraid, and went and hid thy ____ in the earth" (Matthew 25:25)
18. Trusted, with "upon"
19. Potato
20. "I flee unto thee to ____ me" (Psalm 143:9)
23. "____ not thyself because of evildoers" (Psalm 37:1)
26. European lang.
27. "Leah was ____ eyed" (Genesis 29:17)
28. Ripped
30. "If thou seek him with all thy ____" (Deuteronomy 4:29)

33. Favorite
34. Sighing sound
36. "He casteth forth his ____ like morsels" (Psalm 147:17)
38. Compass dir.

by Janet W. Adkins

ACROSS

1. Belonging to the Jairite who "was a chief ruler about David" (2 Samuel 20)
5. Lures
7. "Even of your lusts that ____ in your members" (James 4:1)
8. Name for a boy in Barcelona?
10. French export, to Emile
11. Really (arch.)
13. "Without the word be ____ by the conversation of the wives" (1 Peter 3:1)
14. New cars on the road
15. Person concerned with (suffix)
17. "But the righteous into life ____" (Matthew 25:46)
19. Advantage
21. City near Bethel
22. Electric ____
23. "But ____ thing is needful" (Luke 10:42)
24. Irish Pop
25. "And put a ____ to thy throat" (Proverbs 23:2)
27. "If he that cometh preacheth ____ Jesus" (2 Corinthians 11:4)
29. Ford model
30. Formerly Persia
31. Shem's home, for a while
32. Prayer
34. Hirt, and others
35. Region in NE Poland with many lakes (abbr.)
36. Like alt.
37. Person afflicted with tuberculosis (colloq.)
39. "Esau, who is ____ " (Genesis 36:1)

DOWN

1. Noun-forming suffix
2. Paper measure (abbr.)
3. "I ____ unto Caesar" (Acts 25:11)
4. "I will exalt my throne above the ____ of God" (Isaiah 14:13)
5. To M.D.s, summer scourge
6. Middle-school subj.
7. "Do not drink ____ nor strong drink" (Leviticus 10:9)
9. Bible mount
10. November activity
11. "Then Samuel took a ____ of oil" (1 Samuel 10:1)
12. Biblical exclamation
13. "All knees shall be ____ as water" (Ezekiel 21:7)
14. Joint
16. ____ of the Purple Sage (Z. Grey book)
18. Change for the better
19. In the very near future (arch.)
20. Whim
23. Second son of Judah (Genesis 38)
26. Certain California judge
27. In the vicinity
28. "How long ____ ye between two opinions" (1 Kings 18:21)
30. Release
33. Suitable for (suffix)
34. Farm science (comb. form)
36. "They might only touch the ____ of his garment" (Matthew 14:36)
38. Word in the Great Commission

by Michael J. Landi

ACROSS

1. Place which means "well of the oath" (Genesis 21)
6. Compass dir.
8. Prophet who advised David to go into the land of Judah (1 Samuel 22)
9. U.S. site of a Summer Olympics (abbr.)
10. Where Paul healed Publius' father (var., Acts 28)
11. Judah thought this woman was a prostitute (Genesis 38)
12. Electrical abbr.
13. City also known as Lydda (1 Chronicles 8:12)
16. Where one finds "the street which is called Straight"
17. "he is of ____; ask him" (John 9:21)
18. Esther's Shusan (var.)
20. Pot adjunct
21. City near Bethel (var.)
22. Coral reef
23. Consumed
25. The Great I ____
28. Site of Jesus' first miracle on earth
30. "The Nethinims dwelt in ____, unto the place over against the water gate" (Nehemiah 3:26)
31. "____ sharpeneth ____" [word repeated] (Proverbs 27:17)
34. Right-hand page (abbr.)
35. "For this Agar is mount Sinai in ____" (Galatians 4:25)
37. "David...escaped to the cave ____" (1 Samuel 22:1)
39. His two sons, Hophni and Phine-has, were priests of the Lord
41. Cape Cod state (abbr.)
42. After this Bible book, God did not speak to His people for 400 years (abbr.)
43. River of Egypt
45. "In so doing thou shalt ____ coals of fire on his head" (Romans 12:20)
46. Shammah was the son of this Hararite (2 Samuel 23)
47. Lion of ____ (name of Jesus)
48. "Arise ye, and let us go up to ____ unto the Lord our God" (var., Jeremiah 31:6)
51. Extremely agitated
52. Understand
53. Like a mom's day
54. "The Lord will cut off from ____ head and tail, branch and rush" (Isaiah 9:14)

DOWN

1. Where the handicapped waited "for the moving of the water"
2. Destination of two disciples, when they were joined by the risen Jesus Christ
3. One of seven cities addressed in early chapters of Revelation
4. "I was at Shushan...in the province of ____" (Daniel 8:2)
5. "Who passing through the valley of ____ make it a well" (Psalm 84:6)
6. Continent (abbr.)
7. Son of Shaphan (Jeremiah 29:3)
8. Paul stopped here on his third missionary journey, after Antioch (Acts 18)
10. Home of Gaius and Aristarchus, two of Paul's companions (Acts 19)
14. King who was a remnant of giants (Deuteronomy 3:11)

15. A city of Lycaonia, where Paul fled after Iconium (Acts 14)
19. "The field of blood" (Acts 1)
20. Where the city of Myra was located (Acts 27)
24. Famous seaport on the Mediterranean, in Bible days (var., Ezekiel 26)
26. Shape
27. City where Lydia was converted (Acts 16)
29. "All thy fortresses shall be spoiled, as Shalman spoiled Beth-____" (Hosea 10:14)

32. In parable, five virgins forgot this (Matthew 25)
33. Widow of ____
36. Where Paul's last days were spent
37. Site of Mars' hill
38. Wise men
40. Where Abraham built his second altar (Genesis 12)
44. ____ ink
47. N.T. book (abbr.)
48. Dir.
49. Branch of medicine (abbr.)
50. Greek letter
51. "Hearken unto the voice of ____ cry" (Psalm 5:2)

by Teri Grottke

ACROSS

1. "For they considered not the ____ of the loaves" (Mark 6:52)
7. "In the days of Noah, while the ____ was a preparing" (1 Peter 3:20)
10. "The sons of Carmi; ____" (1 Chronicles 2:7)
11.   Word in a command
12. U.S. state named after Elizabeth I (abbr.)
13. Where the action is
14. "Those that walk in pride he is able to ____" (Daniel 4:37)
16. What the wife of Phinehas named their son (1 Samuel 4)
18. Father of Eliud (Matthew 1:14)
20. City near Bethel
22. "Thy right ____ shall save me" (Psalm 138:7)
23. Used to make powder
24. "Let tears run down like a river...give thyself no ____" (Lamentations 2:18)
26. Former name of Bethel (Genesis 28:19)
28. "The rock poured me out ____ of oil" (Job 29:6)
32. "As he saith also in ____ " (Romans 9:25)
34. Waif, often
35. Compass dir.
36. Related to the camel
38. Forty-niner's destination (abbr.)
39. Father of Ahihud (Numbers 34:27)
41. ____ what?
42. State on the Pacific (abbr.)
43. Redact
44. Roger Williams's state (abbr.)
46. Reach out and touch someone (abbr.)
47. "I ____ hath sent me unto you" (Exodus 3:14)
48. Frustrate
50. "And on the wall of ____ he [Jotham] built much" (2 Chronicles 27:3)
52. "Yet had he the ____ of the spirit" (Malachi 2:15)

DOWN

1. "Is therefore Christ the ____ of sin? God forbid" (Galatians 2:17)
2. Chemical symbol
3. "I am glad of the coming of ...Fortunatus and ____ " (1 Corinthians 16:17)
4. Small fish used as bait
5. Political party in Great Britain
6. Where life and death decisions are made (abbr.)
7. As sons of God, what we can call Him (Galatians 4)
8. Stretch
9. Parent
12. "Surely there is a ____ for the silver" (Job 28:1)
15. Where the Emims were smote, in ____ Kiriathaim (Genesis 14)
17. "____ be thy name" (Luke 11:2)
19. Atlantic seaboard state (abbr.)
21. "And Phares begat ____" (Matthew 1:3)
25. Son of Japheth (1 Chronicles 1:5)
27. Simon ____ (Acts 1)
29. Exec.
30. "The Lord make the woman that is come into thine house like ____" (Ruth 4:11)

31. Slow goer
33. Shade tree
35. Son of Noah
37. "To meet the Lord in the ____"
    (1 Thessalonians 4:17)
40. "He that eateth of this bread
    shall ____ for ever" (John 6:58)
45. Borrower's woe
46. "In all matters of wisdom...the
    king...found them ____ times
    better" (Daniel 1:20)
47. Simile syntax
49. Greek letter
51. Part of middle-school curriculum
    (abbr.)

by Beverley Barnes

ACROSS

1. "We have seen his ____ in the east" (Matthew 2:2)
5. Accepts, in a way
9. Atlantic seaboard state (abbr.)
11. "My ____ is in thee" (Psalm 39:7)
12. Warehouse
13. "Keep me as the ____ of the eye" (Psalm 17:8)
15. ____ de France
17. "My ____ shall praise thee" (Psalm 63:3)
19. Addiction to (suffix)
22. Affirmative (colloq.)
23. "Make thee a fiery serpent, and set it upon a ____" (Numbers 21:8)
24. Printer's measure
26. Secondborn of Adam
30. Cambridge college (abbr.)
31. "At thy word I will let down the ____" (Luke 5:5)
33. One source of evil
35. "The Lord is thy ____ upon thy right hand" (Psalm 121:5)
38. Soloist
39. Peter or Paul (abbr.)
41. Book or teller
42. "The sceptre shall not depart from ____" (Genesis 49:10)
44. "As light of foot as a wild ____" (2 Samuel 2:18)
45. Oft-used abbr.
46. "Put ye in the sickle, for the harvest is ____" (Joel 3:13)
48. Stay ____
50. "Thou hast been a ____ for me, and a strong tower" (Psalm 61:3)
52. ____ is condition
53. Unit of dry measure (abbr.)
54. Complete set of events

55. "Our word...was not yea and ____" (2 Corinthians 1:18)
56. Sauce made with fresh basil
57. Duly noted at a yearly physical (abbr.)

DOWN

1. Hone
2. Hat or heavy
3. "____ thine heart to under standing" (Proverbs 2:2)
4. Depended upon
5. Second letter of the Hebrew alphabet (var.)
6. "They that wait ____ the Lord shall renew their strength" (Isaiah 40:31)
7. Thou, to a non-Quaker
8. Dismantle
10. Masculine nickname
14. Gov't. agency
16. "Consider the ____ of the field" (Matthew 6:28)
18. "Endured the cross, despising the ____" (Hebrews 12:2)
20. ____ cat
21. "A city that is ____ on a hill" (Matthew 5:14)
25. "As an eagle stirreth up her ____" (Deuteronomy 32:11)
27. One who takes to the rails (colloq.)
28. "Bread ____ and to spare" (Luke 15:17)
29. What a bank may do
32. Paul's ____ in the flesh
34. "For there is a ____ sacrifice there for all the family" (1 Samuel 20:6)
36. City on the banks of the Arnon River (Joshua 13:16)

37. Changed hues
40. "Over _____" (wartime favorite)
41. "Get thee behind me, _____"
    (Luke 4:8)
42. Prince of Peace
43. Wed, in Dogpatch
47. Throw things at
49. "Land of the free" (abbr.)
51. System or sphere
53. "_____ of good cheer; I have
    overcome the world"
    (John 16:33)

by Michael J. Landi

ACROSS

1. "There is nothing from without a man, that entering...can ____ him" (Mark 7:15)
4. "At home in the body, we are ____ from the Lord" (2 Corinthians 5:6)
8. Article
9. "____ your enemies" (Matthew 5:44)
11. "Thy rod and thy ____ they comfort me" (Psalm 23:4)
14. "The captain of his host was Abner, the son of ____" (1 Samuel 14:50)
15. "The Lord hath made bare his holy ____" (Isaiah 52:10)
16. "As a ____ doth gather her brood" (Luke 13:34)
17. Celebrated city of Asia Minor, visited by Paul more than once
18. ____ of Sharon (Song of Solomon 2)
20. "The ____ is not to the swift" (Ecclesiastes 9:11)
22. "At the name of Jesus every ____ should bow" (Philippians 2:10)
24. Denial (arch.)
26. Part of a castle
27. "Who can utter the mighty ____ of the Lord?" (Psalm 106:2)
28. King of Israel who was killed by Zimri (var., 1 Kings 16)
29. Linking verb
32. "If any of you lack wisdom, let him ____ of God" (James 1:5)
33. "If thou wilt ____ into life, keep the commandments" (Matthew 19:17)
34. From 1 Corinthians 13: faith, hope, and ____
36. Idol worshiped by Jezebel, among many others
37. Hard ____
40. Not B.C.
41. "Which he ____ on us abundantly through Jesus Christ" (Titus 3:6)
43. Judah's firstborn (Genesis 38:7)
44. Therefore

DOWN

1. "Lest at any time thou ____ thy foot against a stone" (Matthew 4:6)
2. "When thou prayest, ____ into thy closet" (Matthew 6:6)
3. ____ Al, airline known for its security measures
4. "____ not yourselves, but rather give place unto wrath" (Romans 12:19)
5. Son of Zophah (1 Chronicles 7:36)
6. "But let a man ____ himself" (1 Corinthians 11:28)
7. "The tongue can no man ____" (James 3:8)
10. City of Benjamin built or restored by Shamed (1 Chronicles 8:12)
12. "Arise, ye princes, and ____ the shield" (Isaiah 21:5)
13. How to describe Nebuchadnezzar's furnace
19. "The ____ for height, and the earth for depth" (Proverbs 25:3)
21. "Tarsus, a city in ____" (Acts 21:39)
22. Map info

23. "As also in all his ___, speaking in them of these things" (2 Peter 3:16)
25. Past somnolent
30. "For the ___ is red and lowring" (Matthew 16:3)
31. Gypsy ___ (sight in big city)
32. Father of Saul's concubine (2 Samuel 3)
35. "Be not ___ with thy mouth" (Ecclesiastes 5:2)
38. Neh. is part of this
39. Biblical pronoun

42. "Of all that Jesus began both to ___ and teach" (Acts 1:1)

PUZZLE 18

by Michael J. Landi

ACROSS

2. Metamorphosed
10. "He took ____ of his ribs" (Genesis 2:21)
11. Crasher or keeper
12. Partake
13. Missing ingredient in manna
14. Form of "drachma"
16. ____ Aviv
18. "But glory, honour, and ___, to every man that worketh good" (Romans 2:10)
20. Pal, to Philippe
21. ____ in (first point scored after deuce?)
22. Loan
24. "Burning ____ and a wicked heart" (Proverbs 26:23)
26. "He revealeth the ____ and secret things" (Daniel 2:22)
28. Conjunction
30. What April brings
32. "The ____ of all Israel are upon thee" (1 Kings 1:20)
34. One of David's men (1 Kings 1:8)
36. "Sow...in righteousness, ____ in mercy" (Hosea 10:12)
37. "Enter into the rock...for the glory of his ____" (Isaiah 2:10)
39. "But ____ wrought evil in the eyes of the Lord" (1 Kings 16:25)
40. What Isaac named the well at Gerar (Genesis 26:20)
42. Roman emperor with whom Paul had an audience
43. Not A.D.
44. Zaftig, but more bluntly perhaps?
45. "Call me not ___, call me Mara" (Ruth 1:20)
48. "Ye have made the heart of the righteous ____" (Ezekiel 13:22)
49. Aeries

DOWN

1. "Let not sin therefore reign in your ____ body" (Romans 6:12)
2. Do ____!
3. Meal shared by early Christians
4. Hub of a wheel
5. "We pray you in Christ's ___, be ye reconciled" (2 Corinthians 5:20)
6. "____ cities, with walls, gates, and bars" (2 Chronicles 8:5)
7. ____ Sea
8. Feminine name that means "bitter"
9. Rock where Samson lived after slaughter of Philistines (Judges 15)
15. "Come, buy wine and ____ without money" (Isaiah 55:1)
17. Enlighten
19. Head of a family of Gad (var., 1 Chronicles 5:13)
23. Runs swiftly
25. "For the ____ things are passed away" (Revelation 21:4)
27. "Learn first to show ____ at home" (1 Timothy 5:4)
29. "To every man that asketh you a ____ of the hope" (1 Peter 3:15)
31. "____, in all these things we are more than conquerors" (Romans 8:37)
32. Town of the tribe of Dan (Joshua 19:43)
33. Apostles and others
35. At ___-abarim, in the wilderness before Moab, Israelites pitched tents (Numbers 21:11)

38. Chief Philistine city
    (1 Samuel 6:17)
41. New Testament book
46. Its capital is Augusta (abbr.)
47. "For God ____ my witness"
    (Romans 1:9)

by Michael J. Landi

ACROSS

1. Saul fought against them (1 Samuel 14)
6. "There shall they rehearse the righteous ____ of the Lord" (Judges 5:11)
9. "He shall ____ with his teeth, and melt away" (Psalm 112:10)
10. Actress McDaniel
11. "My ____ shall be joyful in my God" (Isaiah 61:10)
12. "Out of thine hand the ____ of trembling" (Isaiah 51:22)
14. Word heard on movie sets
15. Preposition
16. "By the rivers of Babylon, there we ____" (Psalm 137:1)
17. Land of Job
20. "____ unto you, scribes and Pharisees, hypocrites!" (Matthew 23:15)
22. Tenth part of one's income
23. ____ of the Chaldees
24. Town of the tribe of Benjamin (1 Chronicles 8:12)
26. "Go and ____ in the ears of Jerusalem" (Jeremiah 2:2)
27. Joshua, the son of ____
28. Gershwin
31. "The Lord make his ____ shine upon thee" (Numbers 6:25)
32. Word with grade or braid
33. Father of Ehud (Judges 3:15)
34. Scale unit (abbr.)
37. ____ Behind (LaHaye/Jenkins book)
38. "All we like ____ have gone astray" (Isaiah 53:6)

DOWN

1. Item worn by the high priest (Exodus 28)
2. "Because the Lord loved you,...he would keep the ____" (Deuteronomy 7:8)
3. "The tongue is a fire, a world of ____" (James 3:6)
4. Common abbr.
5. "As a jewel of gold in a swine's ____" (Proverbs 11:22)
6. Balaam's beast
7. "They hated knowledge, and did not ____ the fear of the Lord" (Proverbs 1:29)
8. "He went out, and departed into a ____ place" (Mark 1:35)
13. "To see thy ____ and thy glory" (Psalm 63:2)
18. "David took the strong hold of ___: the same is the city of David" (2 Samuel 5:7)
19. Without end
21. Languages (arch.)
23. Father of Michaiah (2 Chronicles 13:2)
25. Greek letter
29. "If ye have ____ as a grain of mustard seed" (Matthew 17:20)
30. "I ____ where I sowed not" (Matthew 25:26)
35. Nephew of Abraham, the son of Nahor (Genesis 22:21)
36. Biblical pronoun

by Janet Kennedy

ACROSS

1. "There sat a certain man at Lystra, ____ in his feet" (Acts 14:8)
7. Recurring chills
10. "When her branch is yet tender...ye know that summer is ____" (Mark 13:28)
11. At the age of (abbr.)
13. Naaman's illness (2 Kings 5)
14. Mischievous child
16. Study of art or science (pl. suffix)
18. Football position (abbr.)
19. Detail for a duffer
20. Stir up
21. Angry
22. Chicago's Lake Shore, for one (abbr.)
23. First name in life preservers?
24. ____ upsmanship
25. ____ Bravo
26. Possessive pronoun
27. "___, and Ammon, and Amalek; the Philistines" (Psalm 83:7)
30. Accountant's abbr.
32. In what state Churchill Downs is found (abbr.)
33. "____ said unto Samuel, Go, lie down" (1 Samuel 3:9)
35. What ___...? (worrywart's favorite question)
36. Small drink
38. "I will not drink henceforth of this fruit of the ____" (Matthew 26:29)
40. Sacrifice site
41. "Yesterday at the seventh hour the ____ left him" (John 4:52)
42. As stated
43. "But the wise took ____ in their vessels" (Matthew 25:4)

44. "Resist the devil, and he will ____ from you" (James 4:7)
45. Female deer (pl.)
46. Organization including Britain, France, and Germany (abbr.)
47. Bring legal action
48. "A certain man...had the ____" (Luke 14:2)
49. Egress

DOWN

1. "Himself took our ___, and bare our sicknesses" (Matthew 8:17)
2. "Come unto ___, all ye that labour" (Matthew 11:28)
3. "And many taken with ___, and that were lame, were healed" (Acts 8:7)
4. Rock worth mining
5. "The man took a golden ____ of half a shekel weight" (Genesis 24:22)
6. Describing a modern take on a classical style
8. Trotting, for one
9. Nero, for one
12. "They...fled unto ____ and Derbe, cities of Lycaonia" (Acts 14:6)
15. "A merry heart doeth good like a ____" (Proverbs 17:22)
17. ____ of many colors
28. Tournament privilege for number-one ranked team
29. Built to keep a river from overflowing
31. "And Lot dwelled in the ____ of the plain" (Genesis 13:12)
34. "Forsake not the Levite as long as thou ____" (Deuteronomy 12:19)

36. Rigged sailboat
37. Paralysis
39. "Which some professing have
    ____ concerning the faith"
    (1 Timothy 6:21)
41. Coming in of the tide
44. Assessment
45. "And whatsoever ye ____ in
    word or deed" (Colossians 3:17)

PUZZLE **21**

by Janet Kennedy

ACROSS

1. "Thou breakest the heads of ____ in pieces" (Psalm 74:14)
7. "Every one that lappeth of the water with his tongue, as a ____" (Judges 7:5)
10. In on
11. Like an aria
12. "____ it ever so humble"
13. Conjunction
14. "Behold behind him a ____ caught in a thicket by his horns" (Genesis 22:13)
17. Loathing
18. Feminine nickname
20. Brit. islands (abbr.)
22. Blue pencil pushers? (abbr.)
23. Printer's measure
24. Wisconsin, the ____ State
27. Catch sight of
30. "I ____ the true vine" (John 15:1)
31. "The hart, and the roebuck, and the fallow ____" (Deuteronomy 14:5)
32. "All ____ like sheep have gone astray" (Isaiah 53:6)
34. Rooster's better half
35. Chicago sight
36. Dad, in Dublin
38. One of the 13 original states (abbr.)
39. "Your adversary the devil, as a roaring ___, walketh about" (1 Peter 5:8)
42. Stags
44. What to do with the frizzies and large felines
46. Greek letter
47. Iron (symbol)
48. Verb in primer's vocabulary
50. Director Lupino

52. Kind of engineer (abbr.)
53. TV network
54. "Shalt thou exalt like the horn of an ____" (Psalm 92:10)

DOWN

1. Discovery zone? (abbr.)
2. "The poor man had nothing, save one little ____ lamb" (2 Samuel 12:3)
3. One of the 13 original states (abbr.)
4. "He shall rule...with a rod of ____" (Revelation 2:27)
5. Expose to air
6. "And I saw heaven opened, and behold a white ____" (Revelation 19:11)
7. Obstinate one, not too kindly
8. Chemical suffix
9. Rocky Mountain ___
15. Mosquito that carries yellow fever
16. Large quantity
19. Preposition
20. "Easier for a ____ to go through the eye of a needle" (Matthew 19:24)
21. Part of psyche
24. Requested (arch.)
25. "She maketh fine linen...and delivereth ____ unto the merchant" (Proverbs 31:24)
26. Harsh
28. Penn's pad? (abbr.)
29. "The king doth not fetch home again his ____" (2 Samuel 14:13)
33. Exclamation of scorn
34. Tortoise's tormentor
37. City near Bethel
40. These may be yoked

41. Division of the United Kingdom (abbr.)
43. "And Peter followed ____ off" (Luke 22:54)
45. Fuss
49. Good or well (prefix)
50. Characteristic of (suffix)
51. Word in a command

by Evelyn M. Boyington

ACROSS

1. Chop off
4. One of Hezekiah's overseers
   (2 Chronicles 31:13)
9. One's own turf?
12. Mother of Hezekiah
    (2 Kings 18:2)
13. Kind of finish
14. "The _____ appeareth, and the
    tender grass showeth itself"
    (Proverbs 27:25)
15. Atlantic seaboard state (abbr.)
16. Altar end of a church
17. "When I _____ the five loaves
    among five thousand"
    (Mark 8:19)
19. New churches, evangelically
    speaking
21. "As for ___, he made havock of
    the church" (Acts 8:3)
22. "I go my ___, and ye shall seek
    me" (John 8:21)
23. Paul or Peter or John or...
26. "A river went out of _____ to
    water the garden" (Genesis 2:10)
28. "Serve him in sincerity and in
    _____" (Joshua 24:14)
29. Masculine nickname
30. City in central Israel
31. "And Abram passed through the
    land...unto the plain of _____"
    (Genesis 12:6)
32. In the ___
33. Jesus conversed in this language
    when on earth (abbr.)
34. "Eldad and _____ do prophesy in
    the camp" (Numbers 11:27)
35. "I will give thee a crown of
    _____" (Revelation 2:10)
36. Day of baptism (two words)
38. Kitchen implement

39. Vainly
40. Progenitor
43. Number of men who met
    Abraham at his tent, including
    the Lord (Genesis 18)
45. _____ in full
46. Conjunction
47. Consume
48. Desire strongly
50. Jane or John
51. "He planteth an ___, and the rain
    doth nourish it" (Isaiah 44:14)
52. Gluts
53. "For ye are all _____ in Christ"
    (Galatians 3:28)

DOWN

1. "Thy word is a _____ unto my
   feet" (Psalm 119:105)
2. "And Joktan begat..._____ and
   Abimael and Sheba"
   (Genesis 10:28)
3. Greek letter
4. "The Lord hath brought me
   home again _____" (Ruth 1:21)
5. Girl in Glasgow
6. Resident (suffix)
7. _____ al
8. "And ___, and Shilhim...all the
   cities are twenty and nine"
   (Joshua 15:32)
9. Biblical verb
10. "Ye shall be as an _____ whose
    leaf fadeth" (Isaiah 1:30)
11. What to do with eggs?
16. One among the covenant sealers
    (Nehemiah 10:26)
18. Make haste
20. Held in fear
21. Flowed or gushed out
    (O.T. spelling)

23. "Women adorn themselves...not with...costly ____" (1 Timothy 2:9)
24. Gold ____
25. Life on the ____ (Dobson book)
26. Ardor
27. Feminine name
28. "Exhort one another daily, while it is called ____" (Hebrews 3:13)
31. Samplings of songs?
32. "Whoso breaketh an hedge, a serpent shall ____ him" (Ecclesiastes 10:8)
34. Darius the ____ (Daniel 11)
35. Master

37. "The voice of ____, and the voice of gladness" (Jeremiah 7:34)
38. Symptoms of malaise
40. "She shall shave her head, and ____ her nails" (Deuteronomy 21:12)
41. "I will cause the sun to go down at ____" (Amos 8:9)
42. The ____ of life (Revelation 22)
43. Prince of Wales, for example
44. Owns
45. Stand ____
49. Apiece (abbr.)
50. Accomplish

by Evelyn M. Boyington

ACROSS

1. Cry
4. Dream or organ
8. ____ team
12. Mouth (pl.)
13. "The children of ____ of Hezekiah, ninety and eight" (Ezra 2:16)
14. Jewelry setting, with no metal showing
15. By means of
16. Nurture
17. Great Lake
18. Masculine name that is an amalgam of Abraham and Noah
20. Make ____
22. Prim and proper
24. In Arthurian legend, the wife of Geraint
25. Writing ____ (what Zacharias asked for in Luke 1)
26. "____ thou not unto his [God's] words" (Proverbs 30:6)
27. Gazelle
30. Biblical exclamation
31. Possessive pronoun
32. "Thou hast enlarged my steps...that my feet did not ____" (Psalm 18:36)
33. Affirmative
34. Compass pt.
35. Obeys, to an AKC member
36. He was a prisoner on Patmos
37. Obliterate
38. Stick
41. Mentally acute
42. Not present and unaccounted for (abbr., pl.)
43. What commandos do
45. Anger
48. Parchment shade

49. "He...saw others standing ____ in the marketplace" (Matthew 20:3)
50. Not (prefix)
51. "And they straightway left their ___, and followed him" (Matthew 4:20)
52. Minister to
53. Our Father

DOWN

1. Absorb
2. Crude metal
3. He accompanied Paul on his first missionary journey
4. Procession
5. Article on a list
6. Legume
7. Missions
8. ____ trap
9. Give notice
10. Like many golfers?
11. What to wear when golfing? (pl.)
19. Nard, olive, et al.
21. Word that precedes day or air
22. Between check-in and check-out
23. "We spend our years as a ____ that is told" (Psalm 90:9)
24. All gone!
27. "Yet ____ grapes shall be left in it, as the shaking of an olive tree" (Isaiah 17:6)
28. Sesame, canola, et al.
29. Usually the east end of a church
31. "For such as be blessed of him shall ____ the earth" (Psalm 37:22)
32. Arid
34. Conjunction
35. Noticed
36. "Even so, come, Lord ____" (Revelation 22:20)

1	2	3		4	5	6	7		8	9	10	11
12				13					14			
15				16					17			
		18	19				20	21				
22	23					24						
25						26				27	28	29
30					31				32			
33				34				35				
		36						37				
38	39	40					41					
42					43	44				45	46	47
48					49					50		
51					52					53		

38. So be it
39. Prepare vegetables for cooking
40. "As the _____ panteth after the water" (Psalm 42:1)
41. Oven
44. Fruit drink
46. One of Pooh's pals
47. "And then shall the _____ come" (Matthew 24:14)

by Evelyn M. Boyington

ACROSS

1. Western state (abbr.)
3. "I gave Egypt for thy ransom, Ethiopia and ____ for thee" (Isaiah 43:3)
7. To do much better than another
12. ____ of the Chaldees
13. From ____ to stern
14. Fabric used to make an ephod
15. In law, an object
17. Preposition
18. "In the beginning was the ____" (John 1:1)
19. "The horse is prepared against the day of ____" (Proverbs 21:31)
21. "Stand in ___, and sin not" (Psalm 4:4)
22. "They fled before the men of ____" (Joshua 7:4)
24. Pres. Clinton's home state (abbr.)
25. Simile syntax
26. "The children of Israel be as the ____ of the sea" (Romans 9:27)
28. Administer the SAT again
31. Quaker pronoun
32. You, in the Yucatan
34. Start
36. Provincetown province (abbr.)
37. Grandfather of David, and son of Ruth
40. Means of communication
43. First word written on the wall (Daniel 5)
44. Linking verb
45. "Two of every ____ shalt thou bring into the ark" (Genesis 6:19)
48. Masculine nickname
49. Took a break
51. "It is as high as heaven...____ than hell" (Job 11:8)
53. Minuscule
54. Naval officer (abbr.)
55. Where one can perspire or be pampered
56. Portion
58. Used by the high priest to hold oil
60. Classified, for one
61. Spread around
62. Altar end of the church
63. Biblical pronoun

DOWN

1. Checks
2. ____ code
3. Christian ed. concern (abbr.)
4. Common abbr.
5. ____ noire
6. "I ____ God, even thy God" (Psalm 50:7)
7. "____ of speech" (how Moses described himself)
8. Employed, in Bible times
9. Conjunction
10. "This I know; for God is for ____" (Psalm 56:9)
11. Printer's measure
16. Day ___
18. "The field is ___, the land mourneth" (Joel 1:10)
20. Three, in Turin
22. "Ramoth with her suburbs, and ____ with her suburbs" (1 Chronicles 6:73)
23. Notion
25. "The ____ of Kish Saul's father were lost" (1 Samuel 9:3)
27. Sighing sound
29. Preposition
30. "The friendship of the world is ____ with God" (James 4:4)

32. Volume
33. Father of Gaal (Judges 9:30)
35. Note on diatonic scale
38. ____ passant (chess term)
39. "If any man ____ to be first, the same shall be last" (Mark 9:35)
41. "Pray for them which despitefully ____ you" (Luke 6:28)
42. Swabs
46. To reward
47. Barter
50. Once more
51. "Behold, the nations are as a ____ of a bucket" (Isaiah 40:15)

52. All ____ (attentive)
53. Pitch
56. Baseball player (abbr.)
57. Like alt.
58. Laughing sound
59. Quadrant in D.C.

by Evelyn M. Boyington

ACROSS

1. Hoover, for example
4. "And I saw, and behold a white ____" (Revelation 6:2)
9. Auction action
12. "Beware of him, and ____ his voice" (Exodus 23:21)
14. "They gave him vinegar to drink mingled with ____" (Matthew 27:34)
15. Shoshonean tribe member
16. Scrambled scuffle
18. "And the Avims which dwelt in ____" (Deuteronomy 2:23)
20. Of considerable size
22. What a raconteur weaves?
23. "And in the fourth chariot ____ and bay horses" (Zechariah 6:3)
26. Cave dweller
27. Partner of rave
28. What Hebron was formerly called, and its namesakes (var., Genesis 35)
30. Preposition
32. ____ white
33. Bypass
34. Queen, for example
35. The royal ____
36. Teams
37. Melted, as a fuse
38. Deface
39. Bees in the bonnet?
41. One husband of Abigail
43. "Let the wicked fall into their own ____" (Psalm 141:10)
44. "God hath blessed thee ____" (two words, Psalm 45:2)
46. Aeries
49. "Manasseh made Judah and the inhabitants of Jerusalem to ____" (2 Chronicles 33:9)
50. "Unto Shem also, the father of all the children of ____" (Genesis 10:21)
52. Holding a grudge
53. ____ station
54. Packs away
55. Tatami (floor ___)

DOWN

1. Title of respect in Brazil and Portugal
2. Lincoln, to his nearest and dearest
3. "As when the ____ fire burneth" (Isaiah 64:2)
5. "Sihon king of the Amorites, and ____ king of Bashan" (Psalm 135:11)
6. Stadium sound
7. Smote
8. "____ the ninth" (1 Chronicles 12:12)
9. Charred
10. Inflammation (suffix)
11. Political partisan (abbr.)
13. Leaven
17. Building extension
19. Ages
21. "Intreat me not to ____ thee" (Ruth 1:16)
23. "The tree ___, and was strong" (Daniel 4:11)
24. "Why do the heathen ____" (Psalm 2:1)
25. Overcome with noise
29. Shaggy mammals
30. ____ there, done that
31. Coniferous trees
33. Achieves success
34. "Their root shall be as rottenness, and their ____ shall go up as dust" (Isaiah 5:24)

36. Bat's bailiwick
37. Pierces
38. "In the resurrection they neither _____ nor are given in marriage" (Matthew 22:30)
40. "Your father hath...changed my wages _____ times" (Genesis 31:7)
41. Feminine name
42. "The reward not reckoned of grace, but of _____" (Romans 4:4)
44. Handful
45. Automobile of a previous generation
47. Singing syllable

48. Jelled
51. Inits. accorded a member of the clergy

by Evelyn M. Boyington

ACROSS

1. With Deborah, he confronted the army of Sisera
5. One of the sons of Merari (1 Chronicles 6:30)
12. Poems
14. Burn with anger
15. Contented comment
17. "And the Lord God caused a ____ sleep" (Genesis 2:21)
19. "Suffer the little children to come unto ____" (Mark 10:14)
20. Apiece (abbr.)
21. Perimeter
23. Farm implements
25. The ____ Pavilions (Kaye novel)
26. Son of Seth
28. "I took the little book...and ____ it up" (Revelation 10:10)
29. In the ____
30. Information
32. Balmy state (abbr.)
33. Spanish pronoun
35. "In the ____ God created" (Genesis 1:1)
37. Exclamation of surprise
39. Concerning, with "in"
40. Oppressed person
42. "I...was come nigh unto Damascus about ____" (Acts 22:6)
44. "The Lord that delivered me out of the ____ of the lion" (1 Samuel 17:37)
46. "Thou art not a ____ of the law, but a judge" (James 4:11)
48. "For the stone shall ____ out of the wall" (Habakkuk 2:11)
49. Mentions
51. Bide a ____ (Scottish phrase)
52. Printer's measure
53. Great Commission verb
54. "The first came out red...and they called his name ____" (Genesis 25:25)
56. Note on the diatonic scale
57. Abandon
60. "____ ye from your evil ways" (2 Kings 17:13)
62. "The God...who hath called us unto his ____ glory by Christ Jesus" (1 Peter 5:10)
63. Daniel's den mates

DOWN

1. Announce loudly
2. Right page (abbr.)
3. "Which of you...can ____ one cubit unto his stature?" (Matthew 6:27)
4. "If ye love me, ____ my commandments" (John 14:15)
6. Resident of the Far East (abbr.)
7. Certain rocks
8. Command to a horse
9. With ____
10. "Then I will give them ____ ____ to know Me" (2 words, Jeremiah 24:7, NKJV)
11. "____ unto me: I will teach you the fear of the Lord" (Psalm 34:11)
13. Actress Ward
16. "Naphtali is a ____ let loose" (Genesis 49:21)
18. "The blessed and only ____, the King of kings" (1 Timothy 6:15)
22. Ruth and Orpah were "women of ____" (Ruth 1)
24. Pronoun
25. Note on the diatonic scale
27. Cheerless

29. Ate out
31. "Strong meat belongeth to them that are of full ____" (Hebrews 5:14)
32. Old-fashioned hand towel message
34. Yield
36. Mature
38. "Moreover the Lord thy God will send the ____ among them" (Deuteronomy 7:20)
41. "My ____ did not slip" (Psalm 18:36)
43. Worried exclamation
44. Greek letter

45. Occident
47. Bridle part
49. ____ fields (what Jesus went through on the sabbath day, Mark 2)
50. Son of Kish
53. European tongue (abbr.)
55. Father of Bezaleel (Exodus 31:2)
58. Quadrant in D.C.
59. British 'bye
61. "And Abram said unto Lot, Let there be ____ strife" (Genesis 13:8)

by Evelyn M. Boyington

ACROSS

1. Member of Congress (abbr.)
4. "Behold, _____ _____ is in thine own eye?" (2 words, Matthew 7:4)
9. Scheduled stopping place (abbr.)
12. Poetic preposition
13. "I will _____ thee seven years" (Genesis 29:18)
14. Handle roughly
15. "There is a friend that sticketh closer than a _____" (Proverbs 18:24)
17. Part of a book
19. Coop comment?
20. Nicholas, for one
21. "The children of Giddel, the children of _____" (Ezra 2:47)
23. "O thou _____ among women" (Song of Solomon 6:1)
26. Excuse me!
27. "Ehud the son of _____ , a Benjamite" (Judges 3:15)
28. Preposition
29. Measure of Everest (abbr.)
30. "This is ___, which was for to come" (Matthew 11:14)
31. "With the _____ of an ass have I slain a thousand men" (Judges 15:16)
32. Continent (abbr.)
33. Nonsense (Brit.)
34. Table or pike
35. "He...shall be called the son of the _____" (Luke 1:32)
38. "The birds of the air have _____" (Matthew 8:20)
39. Towel identification
40. Horned mammal
41. Describing a taskmaster

43. "A man of _____" (Isaiah's description of the Messiah)
46. Long, long time
47. "The sons of Shemidah were...Likhi, and _____" (1 Chronicles 7:19)
49. Greek form of Noah
50. You're all ___!
51. House of _____
52. Compass pt.

DOWN

1. "Will a man _____ God?" (Malachi 3:8)
2. Always (poet.)
3. "That a great _____ is risen up among us" (Luke 7:16)
4. One of the twelve tribes of Israel
5. Horn holler?
6. "Ye do ___, not knowing the scriptures" (Matthew 22:29)
7. Thoroughfare (abbr.)
8. "We have found the _____" (John 1:41)
9. Steeple
10. More than freckled
11. "Stand in ___, and sin not" (Psalm 4:4)
16. Five make one in b'ball
18. Average
20. Stopover on the journey from Egypt to Jordan (Numbers 33:27)
21. Where Joshua was buried: "on the north side of the hill _____" (Judges 2:9)
22. "And the children of Sheshan; _____" (1 Chronicles 2:31)
23. Small, snappish dog
24. Maze instruction
25. Boroughs

Crossword Grid

1	2	3	■	4	5	6	7	8	■	9	10	11
12			■	13					■	14		
15			16				■	17	18			
■		19				■	20				■	■
21	22				■	23					24	25
26				■	27				■	28		
29			■	30				■	31			
32		■	33				■	34				
35		36	37				■	38				
■		39				■	40				■	■
41	42				■	43					44	45
46			■	47	48				■	49		
50			■	51					■	52		

27. To cover up
30. "He became the author of _____ salvation" (Hebrews 5:9)
31. "They have slain them which showed before of the coming of the _____ _____" (2 words, Acts 7:52)
34. Rend
36. Belgian city
37. Pronoun
38. Standards
40. Pester continuously
41. "A time to rend, and a time to _____" (Ecclesiastes 3:7)
42. What a "piggy" is

43. Title of respect
44. "A brother offended is harder to be _____ than a strong city" (Proverbs 18:19)
45. Understand
48. Favorite first word

ACROSS

1. To engrave with acid
4. Common contraction
7. Woodwind
11. Powerful lobby in D.C.
12. Erstwhile emerald?
14. "____ we like sheep have gone astray" (Isaiah 53:6)
15. Proximal's polar opposite
17. Central African nation
19. Gemstone comprising third foundation of wall of the New Jerusalem (Revelation 21)
21. To know (Scot.)
22. Spigot
24. Balaam's beast
25. Marble for marbles?
29. Scold constantly
31. "____ is finished" (John 19:30)
32. Gem in second row of high priest's breastplate (Exodus 28)
33. "I find ____ fault in him" (John 19:4)
34. "And on earth peace, good will toward ____" (Luke 2:14)
36. Bottom of the barrel?
37. "Some of them thought, because Judas had the ____" (John 13:29)
38. Familiar name of Brazilian port
40. Geographical abbr.
42. Gemstone comprising seventh foundation of wall of 19 across
47. Return to original speed (music)
49. Indian communal village
51. Zilch
52. Formerly known as the coney, in Bible times
54. Row
55. Gem in fourth row of 32 across
56. "Thou anointest my head with ____" (Psalm 23:5)
57. Cause disintegration of blood cells

DOWN

1. "But the ____ of all things is at hand" (1 Peter 4:7)
2. Practical joker
3. Converts into cold, hard currency
4. Soft mineral
5. Linking verb
6. To scatter or cluster
8. Tree found on Persian Gulf
9. Not a spring chicken
10. Character actor Jack, whose stock-in-trade was westerns
12. Cohort
13. Conscious self
16. Exposure in Ixtapa?
18. "Go to the ____, thou sluggard" (Proverbs 6:6)
20. Covers with a hard, glossy surface
23. Slender cigars
24. Aspire to
25. First ____
26. Needlefish
27. What to wear
28. Printer's measure
30. ____ and Magog (Revelation 20)
35. Well
37. Young Yankee employee?
39. Measure of resistance
40. Sodium hydroxide
41. One billionth (prefix)
43. Measure of rotations (abbr.)
44. Toy or turkey?
45. Gemstone

46. Light (Lat.)
48. _____ ear
50. Mineral resource
53. Eastern seaboard state (abbr.)

by John H. Thornberg

ACROSS

1. Bashful
4. "Lest thou ____ thy foot against a stone" (Psalm 91:12)
8. "A glorious church, not having ___, or wrinkle" (Ephesians 5:27)
12. Sheltered from wind
13. Gnawing pain
14. Father of Ham, Shem, and Japheth
15. State that is bordered by Illinois (abbr.)
16. "Jesus saith unto them, Come and ____" (John 21:12)
17. Cattle or farm
18. Worship
20. Body parts between the waist and the knees
21. Ironic
22. Engage beforehand
25. Hard fat found in cattle and sheep
27. "The wisdom that is from above is...full of ____ and good fruits" (James 3:17)
28. Affirmative in Acapulco
29. "Your ____ men shall dream dreams" (Joel 2:28)
30. God worshiped by Jezebel, and its namesakes
31. Cotton ____
32. Article
33. Second planet from the sun
34. Small, headless nail
35. Qualities of a bishop: "____, not a brawler" (1 Timothy 3:3)
37. Command to a horse
38. Killer whale
39. One foundation of Christian life
42. "O ye of little ____" (Matthew 8:26)

44. City in Normandy
45. Command word
46. Big blunder
47. "That ye ____ one another" (John 13:34)
48. United
49. Preposition
50. "Hear my voice, and ____ the door" (Revelation 3:20)
51. "That they may be ___, even as we are" (John 17:22)

DOWN

1. Make a mistake
2. "He that hath ears to ____" (Matthew 11:15)
3. Biblical pronoun
4. Jay's love in The Great Gatsby
5. Teen trauma
6. Pronoun
7. "Greater is ____ that is in you" (1 John 4:4)
8. Brisk and lively
9. Composure
10. Canoe component
11. "Hallowed be ____ name" (Matthew 6:9)
16. "Whose waters cast up mire and ____" (Isaiah 57:20)
17. Floppy ones?
19. Astonished
20. Feathered fishing lures
22. Real winner (colloq.)
23. Encompassing the Orient
24. "Charity suffereth long, and is ____" (1 Corinthians 13:4)
25. "For though thou wash thee with nitre, and take thee much____" (var., Jeremiah 2:22)
26. Bone of the forearm
27. Bread from heaven

30. Hardwood tree
31. "The beauty of old men is the
    ____ head" (Proverbs 20:29)
33. "Add to your faith ____"
    (2 Peter 1:5)
34. Noggin
36. What the bread winner must do
37. "But her leaf shall be ____"
    (Jeremiah 17:8)
39. ____ the way
40. First home
41. "And he ____ upon a cherub,
    and did fly" (Psalm 18:10)
42. Airport abbr.
43. Vowel trio

44. To go back on a promise, with
    "out"
47. Biblical exclamation
48. Officer of the U.S. Army (abbr.)

by John H. Thornberg

ACROSS

1. Shushan, per the NIV
5. ____ cake
9. "I therefore so ___, not as uncertainly; so fight I" (1 Corinthians 9:26)
12. Tore
13. The Syrians of ____ (2 Samuel 10, hired by Ammon's heirs to fight David)
14. "Love ____ another" (1 John 4:7)
15. Brother of Jacob
16. Brother of Cain
17. Fuss
18. History
20. Moses' mouthpiece
22. Friendship
25. Alto ____ (jazz instrument)
26. O.T. major prophet (abbr.)
27. Melchizedek, king of ____
30. "O sole ___"
33. Seth's sire
34. Bridle part
35. Together
36. Time of revival (abbr.)
37. "City of David" (Luke 2)
39. What CBS, for one, would like to do: ___Fox?
40. Elemental particles
41. Shake violently
44. Window component
46. Crone
47. Like a funk
49. New Testament book
53. "Love worketh no ____ to his neighbour" (Romans 13:10)
54. Like a certain "ranger"
55. "But ____ found grace in the eyes of the Lord" (Genesis 6:8)
56. Two-____, as tissue
57. Loose ___
58. Times long past

DOWN

1. Compass dir.
2. Moments of elation
3. "Let the ____ roar, and the fulness thereof" (Psalm 96:11)
4. One who votes
5. Peter, for one
6. "And they put on him a purple ____" (John 19:2)
7. Honest one
8. Son of Beor (Numbers 22:5)
9. Deafening din
10. Let go
11. ____ tetra (tropical fish)
19. Yiddish exclamations
21. Get rid of
22. Slightly open
23. Darius the ____ (Daniel 11)
24. Middle Eastern country
25. Father of Enos (Luke 3)
28. Be a party to
29. American ____ (college course, abbr.)
30. Line that separates the earth's crust from its mantle (abbr.)
31. Thing to be done
32. Units of electrical resistance
35. City near Jerusalem
37. Collection
38. ____ Cruces, NM
39. Conjunction
41. Single snack
42. "Then led they Jesus...unto the ____ of judgment" (John 18:28)
43. Unsightly
44. "Here am I, ____ me" (Isaiah 6:8)
45. Mimics

48. Many moons
50. Dove ditty
51. Bituminous pitch
52. Pronoun

PUZZLE 31

by Janet W. Adkins

ACROSS

1. Great amount
5. Lea denizen
8. "All ____ that we should be saved was...taken away" (Acts 27:20)
12. Son of Joah (1 Chronicles 6:21)
13. Gold, in Guatanamo
14. Grandson of Adam
15. "Neither count I my life____ unto myself" (Acts 20:24)
16. Bled, as fabric
17. Used to be
18. Usually 15 percent
20. To ____ for
22. Father of Rachel, and his namesakes
25. Cause great anger
29. Author of Tristram Shandy
30. 911 happy ending
31. Naval officer (abbr.)
32. Laughing syllable
33. "Make a great flame with smoke ____ ____ out of the city" (2 words, Judges 20:38)
37. Belonging to the first son of Eliphaz (Genesis 36:11)
41. "We who are Jews by ____" (Galatians 2:15)
42. "____ ____ Abana and Pharpar... better than all the waters of Israel?" (2 Kings 5:12)
43. Number of performances of a play
44. Day ____
45. Get out of
48. Former Mideast republic (abbr.)
50. Feminine name
54. "When ye ____ the harvest of your land" (Leviticus 23:22)
55. Hwy.
56. She was called "tender eyed"
57. Feminine name
58. Still
59. Writer Bombeck

DOWN

1. "I will ____ evil beasts out of the land" (Leviticus 26:6)
2. Netherlands metropolis
3. Feminine name
4. ____ board
5. "They came and took up his ____, and laid it in a tomb" (Mark 6:29)
6. Mouth (pl.)
7. "And there appeared another ____ in heaven" (Revelation 12:3)
8. "Let them live; but let them be ____ of wood" (Joshua 9:21)
9. Holy ____ of Israel
10. ____ favor (Sp.)
11. Compass pt.
19. "There was no room for them in the ____" (Luke 2:7)
21. Chemical suffix
22. Place of the seal (abbr.)
23. Entrance court (pl.)
24. Untamed one
26. Son of Carmi who was stoned by all of Israel (Joshua 7)
27. Fertilizer from sea birds
28. Shoe width
33. Hosp. employee
34. Continent which includes Italia
35. S.A. country
36. "But the talk of the lips tendeth only to ____" (Proverbs 14:23)
37. Musical instrument of the Old Testament (Isaiah 5)
38. Rather than
39. "____ not with him that flattereth with his lips" (Proverbs 20:19)

40. Elm, for one (abbr.)
45. Eastern state univ.
46. Uncle of Saul (1 Samuel 14)
47. Plug up
49. Consumed
51. Poetic preposition
52. Candidate for a burnt offering
53. Exclamation

by Janet W. Adkins

ACROSS

1. Rouen repository
5. Douglas, for one
8. Father of Gaal (Judges 9:26)
12. Zest
13. Act or process (suffix)
14. "If a man ____ me, he will keep my words" (John 14:23)
15. City in western Germany
16. "Peter...____ unto the sepulchre" (Luke 24:12)
17. Paradise
18. "There shall not be found among you...a charmer...or a ____" (Deuteronomy 18:10–11)
21. Lend an ___
22. Witticism
23. Maximum
26. "Trust in the Lord...and verily thou shalt be ____" (Psalm 37:3)
27. "A brother offended is harder to be ____ than a strong city" (Proverbs 18:19)
30. He was (Lat.)
31. ____ pottage (dish served in Genesis 25)
32. "And Judah and Israel dwelt safely...under his ____" (1 Kings 4:25)
33. Paving material
34. "A golden bell and a pomegranate, upon the ____ of the robe" (Exodus 28:34)
35. With fewer impurities
36. Son of Noah (var., Luke 3)
37. Wrongdoing
38. "He found them ten times better than all the...____" (Daniel 1:20)
43. On a cruise
44. Mini____

45. Pester
47. "God sent him forth from the garden...to ____ the ground" (Genesis 3:23)
48. Work unit
49. Server's advantage, in tennis
50. Unbelievable, as a story
51. Dentist's degree (abbr.)
52. Two nonconsecutive notes on the diatonic scale

DOWN

1. Community consumer org.
2. Elvis' middle name
3. Number of holes on a par-three course, usually
4. "Lest he be wise in his own ____" (Proverbs 26:5)
5. Hubbub
6. Last duke from the line of Esau (Genesis 36)
7. Appointed another appellation
8. "And I will bring forth a seed... and mine ____ shall inherit it" (Isaiah 65:9)
9. Augur
10. At any time
11. Where thieves dwell?
19. Tattle, with "on"
20. Where Cain dwelt (Genesis 4)
23. Rent out
24. Masculine name
25. Spoil
26. Not masc.
27. "I count all things but loss...that I may ____ Christ" (Philippians 3:8)
28. "When we are absent ____ from another" (Genesis 31:49)
29. Father of Abner (2 Samuel 3:23)
31. Separated

32. "Come thou hither...and dip thy morsel in the ____" (Ruth 2:14)
34. "Walk about Zion, and go round about ____" (Psalm 48:12)
35. "They sewed ____ leaves together" (Genesis 3:7)
36. Hesitate
37. "Thou shalt compass me about with ____ of deliverance" (Psalm 32:7)
38. Continent
39. Mimic a merchant
40. Ingredient definitely not found in low-fat recipes
41. Sat high in the saddle

42. "For Paul had determined to ____ by Ephesus" (Acts 20:16)
43. Corporate giant (abbr.)
46. Genetic material

by Janet W. Adkins

ACROSS

1. Ancient Hebrew dry measure (pl.)
5. Fifteenth division of Psalm 119
7. Snare to trap game or fish
8. "And Samuel told him every ____" (1 Samuel 3:18)
10. Weak day? (abbr.)
11. "I am ____ at my very heart" (Jeremiah 4:19)
13. "Lucifer, ____ of the morning! how art thou cut down to the ground" (Isaiah 14:12)
14. "Speakest to ____ the wicked from his wicked way" (Ezekiel 3:18)
15. "La ____" (Debussy composition)
17. Omen; portent
19. Withhold nothing
21. Pronoun
22. Black ____
23. Pronoun for a seaworthy vessel
24. U.S. West Indies territory (abbr.)
25. "And David heard...that ____ did shear his sheep" (1 Samuel 25:4)
27. Knight's steed
29. O.T. book (abbr.)
30. Chinese canine breed
31. Age
32. Lot, to Abraham
34. Foot or footlike structure (zool.)
35. Fencer's gear
36. ____ France
37. "I am like an owl of the ____" (Psalm 102:6)
39. "And the veil of the temple was ____ in twain" (Mark 15:38)

DOWN

1. Give a pink slip
2. "____ I my brother's keeper?" (Genesis 4:9)
3. "____ of the leaven of the Pharisees" (Matthew 16:6)
4. Twenty-first division of Psalm 119
5. "If thou doest not well, ____ lieth at the door" (Genesis 4:7)
6. Liquid measure of ancient Hebrews
7. All ____!
9. To make suitable
10. Like all humans
11. This may be flipped
12. God (Lat.)
13. "They toil not, neither do they ____" (Matthew 6:28)
14. "Son of man, ____ for the multitude of Egypt" (Ezekiel 32:18)
16. "All the ____ run into the sea" (Ecclesiastes 1:7)
18. One who is warded off?
19. Author of Pygmalion
20. Money, in Milano
23. Demonstrate
26. David ____ Gurion
27. Stilton, for one
28. Late actor Will
30. "Be of good ____" (Matthew 9:2)
33. Catalog abbr.
34. "I am counted with them that go down into the ____" (Psalm 88:4)
36. Masculine nickname
38. Printer's measure

by Janet W. Adkins

ACROSS

1. Diva's defining moment
5. One who comes out, familiarly
8. Land measure
12. Preceding portrait or pity?
13. Mist (Scot.)
14. What every word in the Bible is
15. American playwright
16. Stadium sound
17. Actress Daly
18. Imitate
20. Linking verb
22. Birthplace of Saul
25. "The Lord knoweth the thoughts of man, that they are ____" (Psalm 94:11)
29. "In Damascus the governor under ____ the king" (2 Corinthians 11:32)
30. "For how can I ____ to see the evil that shall come unto my people?" (Esther 8:6)
31. Wrongly (prefix)
32. Twelve-step gp.
33. "In lowliness of mind let each ____ other better than themselves" (Philippians 2:3)
37. French painter Pierre Auguste
41. "____ my soul from their destructions" (Psalm 35:17)
42. "Ye were without Christ, being ____ from the commonwealth of Israel" (Ephesians 2:12)
43. Vacuum tube (abbr.)
44. Father of Saul, king of Israel
45. He offered "a more excellent sacrifice" than his brother
48. Exclamation of disbelief
50. Prophetess who awaited the Messiah
54. Used to be
55. Before (poet.)
56. "For thou art a ____ kinsman" (Ruth 3:9)
57. Corn quantity (pl.)
58. N.T. bk.
59. May be

DOWN

1. He succeeded his father, King Abijam (1 Kings 15)
2. Area (abbr.)
3. ____ de la Cite, in Paris
4. "But when thou makest ____ ____, call the poor, the maimed" (2 words, Luke 14:13)
5. Use of force or threats
6. Historical period
7. "Let us ____ ourselves valiantly for our people" (1 Chronicles 19:13)
8. Wait on
9. Wail
10. String of victories
11. Shoe width
19. "Of ___, the family of the Punites" (Numbers 26:23)
21. Sprinted
22. Less spicy
23. Bail out of bed
24. Musical notations
26. Measures used worldwide (abbr.)
27. "____ up a child in the way he should go" (Proverbs 22:6)
28. Parts of a century
34. O.T. bk. (abbr.)
35. Continent (abbr.)

36. _____-ammah, chief city of the Philistines (2 Samuel 8:1)
37. Jacob served Laban seven years for her
38. Father of Hophni and Phineas
39. Belonging to the first month, the month in which Pur was cast (Esther 3:7)
40. Whirlwind near the Faeroe Islands
45. "Stand in ___, and sin not" (Psalm 4:4)
46. Aunt _____ of TV's Mayberry
47. "To _____ is human"
49. Son of Jether (1 Chronicles 7:38)
51. Born (Fr.)

52. Not (Scot.)
53. "Thou hast scattered thine enemies with thy strong _____" (Psalm 89:10)

by Janet W. Adkins

ACROSS

1. Exclamation of sorrow
5. Catalog promise (abbr.)
8. "But ____ found grace in the eyes of the Lord" (Genesis 6:8)
12. Greek form of feminine name that means "princess"
13. ____ wife
14. ____-Lebanon (mountain range in W. Syria, which includes Mt. Hermon)
15. Not ready to turn pro (abbr.)
16. Bone
17. Cave dwellers
18. New Testament epistle
22. The green, green grass of home?
23. ____ of the above
24. Like a sprinter
25. 1/1000th of an inch
28. Exodus character
31. "For ____ be called, but few chosen" (Matthew 20:16)
32. Prevent
33. "Diana...should be destroyed, whom all ____...worshippeth" (Acts 19:27)
34. Employ
35. Biblical verb
36. "Let us ____ before the Lord our maker" (Psalm 95:6)
37. Greek letter
38. "And the ____ gave up the dead which were in it" (Revelation 20:13)
39. "The Lord hath given you the land,...all the ____...faint because of you" (Joshua 2:9)
44. Concept (comb. form)
45. Historical period
46. Tiny amount (colloq.)
48. Bereft; desolate (arch.)
49. Beam of light
50. Masculine name
51. Healing plant
52. Affirmative
53. "Simon ____..."

DOWN

1. Old Testament king whose name means "physician"
2. "For thou art my ____...the Lord will lighten my darkness" (2 Samuel 22:29)
3. Son of Ulla (1 Chronicles 7:39)
4. "O ____ us early with thy mercy" (Psalm 90:14)
5. Progenitor (colloq.)
6. With "down," way to meet the bed
7. "We are perplexed, but not in ____" (2 Corinthians 4:8)
8. Husband of Abigail (1 Samuel 25)
9. Second son of Judah (1 Chronicles 2:3)
10. Members of the bar (abbr.)
11. Possessive pronoun
19. His wife turned into a pillar of salt
20. Part of the psyche
21. Under the weather
24. Texas institute of higher learning (abbr.)
25. Had been
26. Suffix used to form feminine nouns
27. Welcome ____
28. Enzyme of vegetable origin (suffix)
29. Grain mentioned in the Old Testament (Isaiah 28)
30. Suitable for (suffix)

32. "And fire shall consume the
    tabernacles of ____" (Job 15:34)
33. Husband of Sapphira
35. "And there was war between
    ____ and Baasha king of Israel"
    (1 Kings 15:16)
36. Greek island in the Aegean
37. Single speech sound
38. Corset (Brit.)
39. Matinee ____
40. Notorious emperor of Rome
41. *Dies* ____
42. Brother of Job (Genesis 46:13)
43. Don't leave!
44. Longshoremen's org.

47. Solution (abbr.)

ACROSS

1. Don't just sit there
4. "I do __ my bow in the cloud" (Genesis 9:13)
7. Mightier than a machete?
10. Vast desert region (abbr.)
11. Of a certain Indochinese kingdom
12. Enthusiasm
13. "For whom he did foreknow, he also did ____" (Romans 8:29)
16. "Wound for wound, ____ for ____" (clue repeated) (Exodus 21:25)
17. Drunkard
18. Shows or does (suffix)
19. Epitome of wisdom
23. ____ au lait
25. Chums
26. Corrida cheer
27. "They lavish gold...hire a goldsmith; and he maketh it __ __" (2 words, Isaiah 46:6)
28. "They of Persia and of ____... were in thine army" (Ezekiel 27:10)
29. ____ code
30. "Lest I ____ mine own inheritance" (Ruth 4:6)
31. Ancient meeting place, in a city
32. Organ component
33. Omen
35. The Great ____
36. Half of 104, to Hadrian
37. "Ye were ____ with that holy Spirit of promise" (Ephesians 1:13)
40. "Ye are complete in him, which is the head of all ____ and power" (Colossians 2:10)
43. Helps

44. College entrance requirement (abbr.)
45. Three, in Turin
46. Not (Scot.)
47. Atlas, for one (abbr., pl.)
48. Well-spoken affirmative

DOWN

1. Cleopatra's instrument of death, and others
2. "They laid the ark of the Lord upon the ____" (1 Samuel 6:11)
3. "____ shall a man leave his father and his mother" (Genesis 2:24)
4. Drifted off
5. "Rise up, ye women that are at ____" (Isaiah 32:9)
6. Young one
7. Greek philosopher
8. Put on the feedbag
9. Compass dir.
12. Certain chemical compounds
14. Went out on the town
15. Tristran and ____, of the medieval legend
19. Prepare certain dishes
20. "For we...do groan...that ____ might be swallowed up of life" (2 Corinthians 5:4)
21. Oil (comb. form)
22. ____ tide
23. Become one with nature?
24. "For this ____ is mount Sinai in Arabia" (Galatians 4:25)
25. Of a sandy beach
29. "Set me as ____ ____ upon thine heart" (2 words, Song of Solomon 8:6)

31. "When her masters saw that the hope of their _____ was gone" (Acts 16:19)
34. Playground perennial
35. "Ye love the uppermost _____ in the synagogues" (Luke 11:43)
37. "He _____ on the ground, and made clay" (John 9:6)
38. To be (Fr.)
39. Colors
40. _____ fried
41. Long, narrow inlet
42. Doctrine or theory

PUZZLE 37

by Janet W. Adkins

ACROSS

1. Once more; again
5. Egyptian cobra, for one
8. "Launch out...let down your ____ for a draught" (Luke 5:4)
12. Feminine nickname (var.)
13. 1/1000th of an inch
14. "____, lama sabachthani?" (Mark 15:34)
15. With "off," visibly upset
16. Defined time of history
17. Bobbin of a weaver's shuttle
18. Have
20. U.S. medical research org.
22. Woman married (two words)
25. "The Lord is thy ____...thy shade upon thy right hand" (Psalm 121:5)
29. Doesn't pedal
30. "But to him that ____ righteousness shall be a sure reward" (Proverbs 11:18)
31. Assn.
32. Definite article
33. Depended upon
37. "____, which had kept his bed eight years, and was sick of the palsy" (Acts 9:33)
40. What the frontrunner will do
41. One of "the seven churches in Asia" (Revelation 1:11)
42. Long, undetermined time
43. Son of Noah (var., Luke 3:36)
44. Having to do with the community (abbr.)
47. Anger
49. Wood for a funeral rite
53. "____ was a great man among the Anakims" (Joshua 14:15)
55. Corn serving
56. "Not one ____ of his head fall to the ground" (1 Samuel 14:45)
57. Gossip (colloq.)
58. Promotion for a police officer (abbr.)
59. They attend Promise Keepers events

DOWN

1. Corporate giant (abbr.)
2. Jacqueline Kennedy, ____ Bouvier
3. Before (poet.)
4. "But the younger ____ refuse... they will marry" (1 Timothy 5:11)
5. Make ____
6. Title of respect
7. "So Solomon...covered the floor of the house with ____ of fir" (1 Kings 6:14–15)
8. "He shall neither have son nor ____ among his people" (Job 18:19)
9. High priest who raised Samuel
10. High, rocky hill
11. Wrongdoing
19. ____ paint
21. Vowel trio
22. Prepare meat for grilling
23. One of the fenced cities of Naphtali (Joshua 19:38)
24. "Though thou shouldest make thy nest as high as the ____" (Jeremiah 49:16)
26. His name literally means "a stone"
27. Leader Allen of the Green Mountain Boys
28. Father of Joanna (Luke 3:27)

34. Wrath
35. Part of the psyche
36. "The cock shall not crow, till thou hast ____ me thrice" (John 13:38)
37. Express one's opinion
38. Crony (arch.)
39. Maiden in mythology
44. Possessed with a devil
45. Eastern state univ.
46. Where an inch is really an inch (abbr.)
48. Feminine name
50. Sweet potato
51. Grain mentioned in the Old Testament (Isaiah 28)
52. Sea eagle

by Janet W. Adkins

ACROSS

1. ____ water
4. One of Shem's children (Genesis 10:22)
8. Business correspondence abbr.
12. That (Sp.)
13. Latvian monetary unit
14. Composer Stravinsky
15. Becoming slower, in music (abbr.)
16. Layer
17. ____ of the above
18. "____ not at the matter: for he that is higher...regardeth" (Ecclesiastes 5:8)
20. ____ culpa
22. Person concerned with (suffix)
23. Evergreen tree of the cypress family, known for its berries
27. "Thou shalt be missed, because thy ____ will be empty" (1 Samuel 20:18)
29. Source of poi
30. Norma ___, Oscar-winning movie
31. "So Manasseh made Judah and the inhabitants of Jerusalem to ____" (2 Chronicles 33:9)
32. "So will I do for my servants' ____ that I may not destroy them all" (Isaiah 65:8)
33. Carbohydrate (suffix)
34. Resinous substance of South Asia
35. Canned (colloq.)
36. Not brand new
37. Son of Uzziah (Nehemiah 11:4)
39. One (Scot.)
40. Mountain stat.
41. "He is ____ of death" (Matthew 26:66)

44. He helped build the towns of Ono and Lod (1 Chronicles 8:12)
47. Steel beam used in construction
49. Biblical exclamation
50. Presidential power
51. Alley Oop's girlfriend
52. Paving substance
53. "The land is as the garden of ____ before them" (Joel 2:3)
54. Joyeux ____ (holiday greetings in Grenoble?)
55. Sea eagle

DOWN

1. Time in an elected office
2. "All they which dwelt in ____ heard the word of the Lord Jesus" (Acts 19:10)
3. "Let me freely speak unto you of the ____ David" (Acts 2:29)
4. Amend slightly
5. Complain bitterly
6. Gobbled up
7. "But their scribes and Pharisees ____ against his disciples" (Luke 5:30)
8. ____ Peninsula
9. Time past
10. "Unto us a child is born, unto us a ____ is given" (Isaiah 9:6)
11. Before (poet.)
19. Profession of the late James Herriot (colloq.)
21. Son of Seth
23. Father of Agur (Proverbs 30:1)
24. "Woe unto you, scribes and Pharisees...ye compass sea and land to make one ____" (Matthew 23:15)
25. At ____ (heard at boot camp)
26. Bane of oboist?

27. Actress Ward
28. He was (Lat.)
29. "He exacted the silver and... gold...of every one according to his ____" (2 Kings 23:35)
32. Breeze along
36. Iowa institute of higher learning (abbr.)
38. "And Moses told ____ all the words of the Lord" (Exodus 4:28)
39. Related to the sense of hearing
41. Strong wind
42. Speed along
43. Seafarer's woolly tale?

44. Whom the serpent beguiled, ever so subtly
45. Hotel room requirement
46. Summer on the Seine
48. Startling sound

PUZZLE 39

by Janet W. Adkins

ACROSS

1. And so on (abbr.)
4. Describing nonclergy
8. "This ____ Jesus, which is taken up from you into heaven" (Acts 1:11)
12. Gala event, to Gabrielle
13. ____ Domini
14. "The Lord be a ____ and faithful witness" (Jeremiah 42:5)
15. Poetic contraction
16. Welcome benefit or blessing
17. Transportation (colloq.)
18. "All the land of Canaan fainted by ____ of the famine" (Genesis 47:13)
20. "The children of Keros, the children of ____" (Nehemiah 7:47)
22. Uncle of Saul (1 Samuel 14)
23. Fortified rampart
27. Hit TV show
29. "And his ____ went throughout all Syria" (Matthew 4:24)
30. Busy one
31. Untried, as talent
33. "Beggar named Lazarus, which was laid at his gate, full of ____" (Luke 16:20)
34. Singleton, in Strasbourg
35. Doctors' support group (abbr.)
36. Mythological god of war
37. KJV word for "bud," as on a flower (Exodus 25)
38. "I will utter dark ____ of old" (Psalm 78:2)
40. "Lord, if it be thou, ____ me come unto thee on the water" (Matthew 14:28)
41. The year 1501, to Flavius
42. Son of Levi (Numbers 3:17)
45. Continent
48. Change direction slightly
50. Land where Cain dwelt (Genesis 4)
51. What is unfurled
52. Fencing sword
53. Food fish
54. Actress Daly
55. Actress Talbott
56. WWII milieu (abbr.)

DOWN

1. Father of Peleg and Joktan (Genesis 10:25)
2. Noxious weed (Matthew 13)
3. "Create in me a ____ heart, O God" (Psalm 51:10)
4. Apply some elbow grease
5. Therefore (arch.)
6. Ending for many words in Italian
7. Devours
8. "She [Rebekah] said...We have both ____ and provender enough" (Genesis 24:25)
9. Onassis
10. Miry clay
11. Shoe width
19. "I will ____ no wicked thing before mine eyes" (Psalm 101:3)
21. The Philippines, for example, to Rene
23. Uncovers
24. "And he brought forth the spoil of the city in great ____" (2 Samuel 12:30)
25. Nevada city
26. "Thou wilt ____ him in perfect peace" (Isaiah 26:3)
27. Times of historical significance
28. "In ____ was there a voice heard, lamentation, and weeping" (Matthew 2:18)

1	2	3		4	5	6	7		8	9	10	11
12				13					14			
15				16					17			
18			19				20	21				
		22				23				24	25	26
27	28				29					30		
31		32		33						34		
35				36				37				
38			39					40				
			41				42				43	44
45	46	47			48	49				50		
51					52					53		
54					55					56		

29. "Be of good cheer; thy sins be _____ thee" (Matthew 9:2)
32. "After the _____ which they call heresy, so worship I the God" (Acts 24:14)
33. "A foolish man, which built his house upon the _____" (Matthew 7:26)
37. "In the night _____ of Moab is laid waste, and brought to silence" (Isaiah 15:1)
39. Another word for idol
40. City of Macedonia where Paul preached

42. "With them in the clouds, to _____ the Lord in the air" (1 Thessalonians 4:17)
43. "For he shall grow up...as a _____ out of a dry ground" (Isaiah 53:2)
44. _____ the seer (2 Chronicles 12:15)
45. Rear of a ship
46. Cunning
47. John (Scot.)
49. On or upon (prefix)

PUZZLE 40

by Janet W. Adkins

ACROSS

1. Juliette Low's organization (abbr.)
4. Depot (abbr.)
7. ____ reliever
11. "The ____ state of that man is worse than the first" (Luke 11:26)
13. Desire
14. Competent
15. Theory
16. Old auto
17. Wild goat
18. Stinging comment
19. Welfare; benefit
21. "And ____ also the Jairite was a chief ruler about David" (2 Samuel 20:26)
23. Part of a day (abbr.)
24. One-____ is a tithe
27. Righteous, symbolical name of Israel (var.)
32. One of Lamech's two wives (Genesis 4:19)
33. Conjunction
34. Late folk singer Laura
35. David's nephew (2 Samuel 13:3)
38. "Yet through the ____ of water it will bud, and bring forth boughs" (Job 14:9)
39. Certain therapist (abbr.)
40. Kitchen necessity
41. "Can two walk ____" (Amos 3:3)
46. "____ it Romantic?"
49. Inter ____
50. On or upon (prefix)
51. Unit of weight in the Middle East
52. Practices fabrication
53. ____ Perce, North American Indian tribe

54. Heads
56. Center; source
57. Understand; realize
58. "____ unto you, scribes and Pharisees" (Matthew 23:14)

DOWN

1. Speaking too easily
2. Actress Thompson
3. Tribe to which Anna the prophetess belonged (Luke 2)
4. Mideast country
5. Problem child?
6. "And he [Samson] said...then shall I be weak, and be as ____ man" (Judges 16:11)
7. Matched set
8. French clergy member
9. Channel, Solomon, Hawaiian, et al., to Christophe
10. ____! (word heard in a queue)
12. Aka Dorcas (Acts 9)
20. Sounds of hesitation
22. ____ factor (group of antigens)
24. ____ Mahal
25. People living in southern Nigeria
26. Feminine nickname
27. Patient and faithful sufferer
28. "But ye have an ____ from the Holy One, and ye know all things" (1 John 2:20)
29. Deli loaf
30. Footed vase
31. ____ a chance
36. Period
37. Site of Mars' hill
38. Thus
40. "In a race run all, but one receiveth the ____" (1 Corinthians 9:24)
41. Bath powder

1 2 3 4 5 6 7 8 9 10
11 12 13 14
15 16 17
18 19 20
21 22 23
24 25 26 27 28 29 30 31
32 33 34
35 36 37 38
39 40
41 42 43 44 45 46 47 48
49 50 51
52 53 54 55
56 57 58

42. Highly spiced stew
43. The ____ eagle (fowl not to be eaten; Leviticus 11:18)
44. "Among these nations shalt thou find no ____" (Deuteronomy 28:65)
45. Fencer's adjunct
47. Garbage ____
48. Mount ____, in the land of Moab, gateway to Canaan (Deuteronomy 32)
55. Compass point

PUZZLE 41

by Janet W. Adkins

ACROSS

1. "For ____ have sinned, and come short of the glory of God" (Romans 3:23)
4. ____ Miner's Daughter (Loretta Lynn film biography)
8. ____ California
12. Misery
13. "He died unto sin ___: but in that he liveth" (Romans 6:10)
14. Son of Shobal (Genesis 36:23)
15. "Angels which kept not their first ____" (Jude 6)
17. In close proximity
19. "Kiss the Son, ____ he be angry, and ye perish" (Psalm 2:12)
21. Alaskan outpost
22. Extinct creatures
25. Upper ____
27. Calm; tranquil
28. Where Stephane keeps his savings
29. Young man
32. "Thou shalt dwell in the land of Goshen, and thou shalt ____ ____ unto me" (2 words, Genesis 45:10)
34. "Thy ___, O God, is for ever and ever" (Psalm 45:6)
36. What old colleges do?
37. Hand (Sp.)
39. The Thin Man's (of moviedom) best friend?
40. Simon ___
41. "____ ye in at the strait gate" (Matthew 7:13)
42. Son of Eliphaz (Genesis 36:11)
45. What crowed thrice (Matthew 26)
47. "The governor under ____ the king kept the city of the Damascenes" (2 Corinthians 11:32)

49. One like Mr. Dithers (of the comics), and others
53. With 20 Down, singing syllables
54. First murder victim
56. Retirement acct.
57. Printer's measure
58. Darius the ___, ruler of Babylon
59. See ___

DOWN

1. "Stand in ___, and sin not" (Psalm 4:4)
2. ____ Alamos
3. "____ all the earth fear the Lord" (Psalm 33:8)
4. Shelters for farm animals
5. Individuals
6. Dog days demand (abbr.)
7. Where the cedars were acclaimed (abbr.)
8. "____ Buddies" (short-lived 80s TV sit-com)
9. City in southern Judah (Joshua 15:50)
10. Color of green
11. Church denomination (abbr.)
16. "He sitteth ____ and keepeth silence" (Lamentations 3:28)
18. He "walked with God"
20. With 53 Across, singing syllable
22. "Him that worketh is the reward not reckoned of grace, but of ____" (Romans 4:4)
23. Preposition
24. "If any man will come after me, let him ____ himself" (Matthew 16:24)
26. Aware of what's really happening (colloq.)
28. "Doth the wild ass ____ when he hath grass?" (Job 6:5)

29. "For the Son of man is come to save that which was ____" (Matthew 18:11)
30. To pay one's share (colloq.)
31. "Neither count I my life ____ unto myself" (Acts 20:24)
33. ____ Colonies, Iowa historic communities
35. Holds a certain position
38. Group that advises the President (abbr.)
40. God allowed him to harm Job
41. School (Fr.)
42. "We spend our years as a ____ that is told" (Psalm 90:9)

43. Head of the Eranites (Numbers 26:36)
44. Honey, in the pure, clarified form
46. Father of Jesse
48. Masculine nickname
50. Title of respect
51. Poetic contraction
52. Got the blues
55. "____ sober" (1 Peter 5:8)

PUZZLE 42

by Janet W. Adkins

ACROSS

1. Rascal
4. Le Cote ____ (W. Africa region)
7. Son of Enoch (Genesis 4:18)
11. Woman was made from ____ ____ (2 words)
13. Her name means "life"
14. Spy (colloq.)
15. ____ de soie (rich, silken material)
16. Fall flower, for short
17. "A flattering mouth worketh ____" (Proverbs 26:28)
18. Of considerable size, as a drink
19. "And Israel dwelt in all the cities of the ____" (Numbers 21:25)
21. Used to be
23. WWII red-letter day (abbr.)
24. "A virtuous ____ is a crown to her husband" (Proverbs 12:4)
27. "And Saul smote the Amalekites from ____ until...Shur" (1 Samuel 15:7)
32. "And Israel...spread his tent beyond the tower of ____" (Genesis 35:21)
33. "Therefore God...hath anointed thee with the ____ of gladness" (Psalm 45:7)
34. One conquered by Persia
35. Stringed instrument resembling a lyre, in the Bible
37. Aussie tennis great
38. And (Fr.)
39. ____ Harbor, NY
40. "Lest...when I have preached to others, I...should be a ____" (1 Corinthians 9:27)
45. ____ the Terrible, Russian czar
49. Ancient Hebrew dry measure
50. Broadcast

51. Mount ____, in the land of Moab (Deuteronomy 32)
52. Bill of fare
53. Louis XV, par exemple
54. First name in murder mysteries (and Perry's creator)
55. ____bellum South (period following Civil War)
56. Gov't. drug prevention org.
57. Affirmative

DOWN

1. Like Queeg or Bligh (abbr.)
2. ____ code
3. Popular soap
4. "Luke, the beloved physician, and ___, greet you" (Colossians 4:14)
5. Mature female cell
6. Dismissal
7. Son of Bani (1 Chronicles 9:4)
8. Defeat utterly
9. "When he speaketh ____ ____, he speaketh of his own" (2 words, John 8:44)
10. Cubs' "cribs"?
12. Fortress
20. N.T. book (abbr.)
22. Article
24. NBA great Unseld
25. Harem room
26. Son of (Scot., prefix)
27. Used physical force
28. "How long will ye ____ mischief against a man?" (Psalm 62:3)
29. O.T. book (abbr.)
30. Summer drink
31. Pronoun
33. "For which cause we faint not;...though our ____ man perish" (2 Corinthians 4:16)

36. Feminine nickname
37. Calif. city
39. Mideast country
40. Unconscious condition
41. "So be it"
42. Faxed
43. Factual and actual
44. Vowel quartet
46. "Every thing that he had made...
   was _____ good" (Genesis 1:31)
47. Skilled; competent
48. Greek form of father of Shem,
   and his namesakes

PUZZLE 43

by Janet W. Adkins

ACROSS

1. Father, by another name
5. Possesses
9. "Why make ye this ___, and weep?" (Mark 5:39)
12. Idol worshiped
13. "How beautiful are the ____ of them that preach the gospel" (Romans 10:15)
14. Receptacle
15. Summers on the Seine
16. "Lest he ____ my soul like a lion, rending it in pieces" (Psalm 7:2)
17. Shakespearean sonnet, perhaps
18. "Let us therefore come boldly unto the ____ of grace" (Hebrews 4:16)
20. "The spirit truly is ___, but the flesh is weak" (Mark 14:38)
22. School subj.
24. "Therefore if thine ____ hunger, feed him" (Romans 12:20)
26. Stern, nautically speaking
28. Tennis call
30. ____ of the Chaldees
31. Simon ___-Jona
32. Preposition
33. Sibling, for short
35. "____ will not forsake thee" (Deuteronomy 4:31)
36. "Unto Shem also, the father of all the children of ____" (Genesis 10:21)
38. Big ___
39. "For his ____ endureth but a moment" (Psalm 30:5)
41. Biblical exclamation
43. The witch of ____ (visited by Saul)
45. Prophet of God who convicted David of his sin

50. Organization similar to 4-H (abbr.)
51. Hardy cabbage
53. Vigorous
54. Brand name to "dye" for
55. "Feed me...for I am faint: therefore was his name called ____" (Genesis 25:30)
56. Feminine name
57. ____ a girl!
58. Like most gossips
59. Sea mammal

DOWN

1. Aid in wrongdoing
2. Noted hot springs locale
3. TV's "Beverly Hillbillies" actor
4. Besides
5. "O Jerusalem, Jerusalem...how ____ would I have gathered thy children" (Matthew 23:37)
6. Tiny
7. Not too far away
8. "Arise, and go into the ____ which is called Straight" (Acts 9:11)
9. Dwelling
10. Greek form of Thomas
11. Bill of currency
19. Take-home pay
21. Article
23. "The ____ of the Lord shone round about them" (Luke 2:9)
25. Part of a century (abbr.)
26. Twelve-step group (abbr.)
27. "For he that is dead is ____ from sin" (Romans 6:7)
29. Sound of hesitation
31. "They are faithful and beloved, partakers of the ____" (1 Timothy 6:2)

32. Iron (abbr.)
33. "_____ habla Espanol"
34. Preposition
35. Laughing syllable
37. "The sacrifices of God are a _____ spirit" (Psalm 51:17)
38. Sheep's comment
40. Irritating insects
42. "Thou hast been...a strong tower from the _____" (Psalm 61:3)
44. Famed watchmaker
46. "_____ same Jesus, which is taken up from you into heaven" (Acts 1:11)
47. Tortoise's tormentor

48. Egyptian dancing girl
49. Actress Patricia
50. Day of the wk.
52. _____ Alamos

PUZZLE 44

by Janet W. Adkins

ACROSS

1. Singer Garfunkel
4. WWII fliers (abbr.)
7. Poet Teasdale
11. "Serve him with all your heart and with all your ____" (Deuteronomy 11:13)
13. Actress Gardner
14. Freshman at West Point (var.)
15. Father (Aramaic)
16. Not mentioned in another place (abbr.)
17. Opposite of windward
18. "For rebellion is as the sin of ____" (1 Samuel 15:23)
21. Nineteenth U.S. president
23. Vowel trio
24. "____ and friend hast thou put far from me" (Psalm 88:18)
25. Take a ___
26. Article
29. Ancient Hebrew dry measure
30. ____ ear
31. Win, place, or ___
32. ____ capita
33. Form a lap?
34. "The Lord make his face ____ upon thee" (Numbers 6:25)
35. Masculine nickname
36. "Heal the sick, cleanse the lepers, ____ the dead" (Matthew 10:8)
37. "He smote his neighbour unwittingly, and hated him not ____" (Joshua 20:5)
41. Once more; again
42. Used to be
43. "Do good, and ___, hoping for nothing again" (Luke 6:35)
47. Animal shelter
48. Linking verb
49. "He being not a forgetful hearer, but a ____ of the work" (James 1:25)
50. Tribe of the prophetess Anna
51. ____ of man
52. Beans or sauce

DOWN

1. King of Judah, after his father Abijam (1 Kings 15)
2. Embezzle
3. Vat
4. Carries on
5. Opposite of sans
6. "They were all amazed,...saying, We never saw it on this ____" (Mark 2:12)
7. Show mercy
8. ____ breve (music)
9. Sand bar
10. Be a party to mischief
12. One who's passed the bar?
19. Person concerned with (suffix)
20. Lea denizen
21. Base in baseball
22. State unequivocally
24. Cut off
25. Bridle part
26. Not that
27. Sharpen
28. "Hey, ___!" bleated the goat
30. "Now the ____ ____ the time of the firstripe grapes" (2 words, Numbers 13:20)
31. "But thou, O Lord, art a ____ for me" (Psalm 3:3)
33. Title of respect
34. Uncle ___
35. Ivory ____ (where a prof resides, maybe)
36. "He is ___!" (Easter exultation)

37. "Who passing through the valley
    of ____ make it a well"
    (Psalm 84:6)
38. Son of Seth
39. Treat like the guest of honor
40. Poi source
44. Identified with the Roman
    Aurora (Gr. myth.)
45. Latest (comb. form)
46. "My flesh longeth for thee in a
    ____ and thirsty land"
    (Psalm 63:1)

PUZZLE 45

by Janet W. Adkins

ACROSS

1. King of the Amalekites, whose life Saul spared
5. Sibling, familiarly
8. French cleric
12. ____ 18 (Uris novel about Warsaw Ghetto)
13. Unfortunate occurrence (arch.)
14. Father of Eliasaph (Numbers 3:24)
15. Contemporary
16. When this org. meets, there are plenty of doctors in the house
17. "The ____ are a people not strong" (Proverbs 30:25)
18. "Give thanks at the ____ of his holiness" (Psalm 97:12)
21. Poetic contraction
22. "I will ____ you out of their bondage" (Exodus 6:6)
23. In a line
26. Preposition
27. Tell on (colloq.)
30. Soft fabric
31. "If any man be in Christ, he is a ____ creature" (2 Corinthians 5:17)
32. San ___, CA
33. Masculine nickname
34. Work outside the home?
35. One of Japheth's sons (Genesis 10:2)
36. First name in Exodus, Uris novel
37. Mother ____
38. "Are they not all ____ spirits, sent forth...for them who shall be heirs" (Hebrews 1:14)
43. "The Lord is my strength and ____" (Exodus 15:2)
44. Row
45. Yearn for
47. Rabbit relative
48. Mine (Ital.)
49. Cowboy portrayer Jack
50. Son of Salah (Genesis 10:24)
51. Church officer (abbr.)
52. Soaks flax

DOWN

1. Measure of electrical power
2. Inedible fowl (Leviticus 11:18)
3. Toward the sheltered side, nautically
4. "And when I heard this thing, I rent my ____" (Ezra 9:3)
5. "The nations have heard of thy ____, and thy cry hath filled the land" (Jeremiah 46:12)
6. Poetic foot
7. "Yea, the ____ hath found an house" (Psalm 84:3)
8. "____ ____ flowing with milk and honey" (2 words, Exodus 3:8)
9. Where interest accrues, in France
10. ____ noire
11. They loop the Loop
19. Work unit
20. Broadcast on TV
23. Toward the stern of the ship
24. He surrendered at Appomattox
25. Not a spring chicken
26. "The harvest truly is great, but the labourers are ____" (Luke 10:2)
27. "Will a man ____ God?" (Malachi 3:8)
28. "And ____ did that which was right in the eyes of the Lord" (1 Kings 15:11)

29. _____ Aviv
31. "There fell a _____ and grievous sore upon the men which had the mark of the beast" (Revelation 16:2)
32. "[Elijah] sat down under a _____ tree: and he requested...that he might die" (1 Kings 19:4)
34. High-tech medical test (abbr.)
35. Province (abbr.)
36. "And the _____ of the Lord was kindled against Moses" (Exodus 4:14)
37. King of Judaea at Christ's birth
38. Ruth and Orpah's homeland

39. Concerning
40. Canine emotional barometer
41. River formed at Khartoum
42. Pesky insect
43. Pronoun
46. Printer's measures

by Janet W. Adkins

ACROSS

1. "He [Jesus] went into the syna-gogue...and stood up for to ____" (Luke 4:16)
5. ____ Sea
8. Become wan
12. Inter ____
13. Mother lode
14. "For this ____ is mount Sinai in Arabia" (Galatians 4:25)
15. "Thou shalt lend unto ____ nations, and thou shalt not borrow" (Deuteronomy 28:12)
16. More, in Managua
17. Showy flower
18. Be quiet!
20. Where Esther lived, but not Mordecai
22. ____ Pan Alley
23. Belonging to a town near Bethel (Joshua 7)
24. Father of Jeroboam (1 Kings 16:3)
27. Drug prescription abbr.
28. Tore
31. Sixth month of the Jewish year
32. Mideast alliance (abbr.)
33. ____ it!
34. French possessive pronoun
35. Feminine name
36. "But let us watch and be ____" (1 Thessalonians 5:6)
37. Work unit
38. Summer home staple
39. Where Jesus delivered "The Olivet Discourse"
46. Goofs
47. Patriotic org.
48. Sacred vow
49. Brand name in sauces
50. Pot adjunct
51. She sailed in 1492
52. Born (Fr.)
53. Parts of a century (abbr.)
54. Hidden obstacle

DOWN

1. Candidates for offerings, as in burnt
2. King of Israel, while Asa reigned over Judah (1 Kings 16)
3. Indigenous, ethnic group of Japan
4. "Until the...dawn, and the ____ ____ arise in your hearts" (2 words, 2 Peter 1:19)
5. CD____ (computer adjunct)
6. Historical time period
7. "We are perplexed, but not in ____" (2 Corinthians 4:8)
8. Old-fashioned fire fighters' needs
9. Site of the Taj Mahal
10. Describing nonclergy
11. Gaelic
19. Direct ____
21. First ____
24. War zone, of the not too distant past (colloq.)
25. Netherlands city
26. ____ relief
27. Catch some rays
28. "To turn aside the needy...that they may ____ the fatherless!" (Isaiah 10:2)
29. Fifth or Madison, e.g.
30. Uncle of Saul (1 Samuel 14:50)
32. "Blessed is the man that walketh not in the counsel of the ____" (Psalm 1:1)
33. Parts of parliamentary procedure
35. Biblical verb

36. Costa del ___
37. "Let him seek peace, and ____ it" (1 Peter 3:11)
38. "He had made a scourge of small ____" (John 2:15)
39. Body of water, in Boulogne
40. Algerian seaport
41. Encourage
42. Not biased
43. "For ____ is the help of man" (Psalm 60:11)
44. Sicilian volcano
45. Carpet quality

by Janet W. Adkins

ACROSS

1. She played Nora to Powell's Nick
4. Balaam's bane
7. Father of Saul (Acts 13)
10. Mimic
11. O.T. book (abbr.)
12. "Through faith also ____ ...received strength to conceive" (Hebrews 11:11)
13. One quality of God
16. Like blustery, cold weather
17. First manners lesson word
18. Grain
20. Title given to Italian monk
21. "Blessed are they whose...sins are ____" (Romans 4:7)
25. Depressed
27. "I ____ on the work of thy hands" (Psalm 143:5)
28. Christmas ___
29. Girl (Scot.)
30. Found in veins?
31. ____ canto, singing style
32. Shoshonean
33. ____ Scott decision, landmark legal case
34. Roll call answer
35. "who hath ____ of eyes?" (Proverbs 23:29)
37. Seasoning (Fr.)
38. Shoe width
39. Heats to almost boiling
42. "The Lord said unto him [Solomon], I have heard thy prayer and thy ____" (1 Kings 9:3)
45. Retirement accts.
46. Its members trace their ancestors to the Mayflower (abbr.)
47. Plain of ____ (Nehemiah 6:2)
48. Kin (abbr.)
49. Consumed
50. ____ Paltz, NY

DOWN

1. "Thy word is a ____ unto my feet" (Psalm 119:105)
2. European auto maker
3. "Because I have called, and ____ ____" (2 words, Proverbs 1:24)
4. Feminine name (var.)
5. Ump's call
6. Texas college (abbr.)
7. ____ blanche
8. Gershwin
9. Maxim; proverb
14. "Lest at any time your hearts be overcharged with...____ of this life" (Luke 21:34)
15. Let free
19. Park, for one (abbr.)
21. "Behold, I cast out devils, and I do ____" (Luke 13:32)
22. "For ____ is as the sin of witchcraft" (1 Samuel 15:23)
23. At any time
24. Editor's mark
25. To obscure
26. Fashionably ____
27. "Let me set a ____ of bread before thee" (1 Samuel 28:22)
33. "Praise the Lord from the earth, ye dragons, and all ____" (Psalm 148:7)
34. Miami pro team
36. Himalayan country
37. Give goosebumps
39. Scram!
40. Finished
41. "Drought and heat consume the ____ waters" (Job 24:19)

42. Title of respect
43. Actress Mary
44. Director Lupino

by Janet W. Adkins

ACROSS

1. Feminine name
4. "All the trees of the field shall
   ____ their hands" (Isaiah 55:12)
8. State, Main, etc.
11. Johnny ____
12. Lucifer
13. Biblical exclamation
14. First name of Greek magnate
15. One (comb. form)
16. Confederate general Jubal
18. Easter time
20. Civil rights activist Guinier
21. O.T. book
22. Aloof
25. Geometrical shape
26. Main part of the church building
   (pl.)
27. Buckeye state (abbr.)
28. "Stand in ____, and sin not"
   (Psalm 4:4)
29. Linking verb
30. "Asahel was as light of foot as a
   wild ____" (2 Samuel 2:18)
31. Quadrant in D.C.
32. Brother of Rebekah
34. "Yet he abideth faithful: he
   cannot ____ himself"
   (2 Timothy 2:13)
35. "When I shall send ____ unto
   thee, or Tychicus" (Titus 3:12)
37. "Cursed be every ____ that
   curseth thee" (Genesis 27:29)
38. "I am weak: O Lord, ____ me;
   for my bones are vexed"
   (Psalm 6:2)
39. Reveal
41. "Ye ask, and receive not,
   because ye ask ____" (James 4:3)
43. Father of Saul
44. Pale

47. "I count all things but loss...that
   I may ____ Christ"
   (Philippians 3:8)
48. Son of Enan (Numbers 1:15)
50. Compass dir.
51. Record of progress
52. Replied
53. Moisture

DOWN

1. Retirement acct.
2. German article
3. Texas town
4. Metric measure (abbr.)
5. 28 x 2, to Tiberius
6. "And Joshua sent men from
   Jericho to ____" (Joshua 7:2)
7. Aim to satisfy
8. Mideast country
9. ____ Aviv
10. ____ what?
12. Grayish brown color
17. "The ____ are a people not
   strong" (Proverbs 30:25)
19. "As the serpent beguiled ____
   through his subtlety"
   (2 Corinthians 11:3)
20. Bring cheer
21. "For thou hast made him a little
   ____ than the angels" (Psalm 8:5)
22. Belonging to the fifth son of
   Zerah (1 Chronicles 2:6)
23. "____ ____ comes to the Father
   except through Me"
   (2 words, John 14:6, NKJV)
24. Not we
25. "And...there was a marriage in
   ____ of Galilee" (John 2:1)
26. "David heard in the wilderness
   that ____ did shear his sheep"
   (1 Samuel 25:4)

30. "Thy youth is _____ like the eagle's" (Psalm 103:5)
32. Sheltered place (pl.)
33. Belonging to Absalom's captain of the host (2 Samuel 17:25)
34. Of gold (Fr.)
36. Object
39. Coach of the Indiana Pacers
40. Good king of Judah (1 Kings 15)
41. Hole-making tool
42. Mine (Ital.)
43. Ripe old age, in Rome
45. Chemical suffix
46. "And he hath put a _____ song in my mouth" (Psalm 40:3)

49. Laughing sound

by Janet W. Adkins

ACROSS

1. Dr. Zhivago heroine
5. Metric land measure (abbr.)
8. Bone or breaker
11. Ancient Hebrew dry measure
12. Feminine name
14. N.A. country
15. "Avenge not yourselves, but rather ____ ____ unto wrath" (2 words, Romans 12:19)
17. Knight's form of address
18. Actress Ullmann
19. "____ hath desired to have you, that he may sift you" (Luke 22:31)
21. "Shall seven years of ____ come unto...thy land?" (2 Samuel 24:13)
24. Indian princess
25. Southern state (abbr.)
26. Turmoil
28. "Give not that which is holy unto the ____" (Matthew 7:6)
30. Shoe width
31. Bog
33. Provide the means
35. Compass dir.
36. Thing on a list
37. "And your children shall ____ in the wilderness forty years" (Numbers 14:33)
40. Like an ump
42. Circular ____ (junk mail repository?)
43. Formerly Clay
44. "Dearly beloved, ____ ____ yourselves...I will repay" (2 words, Romans 12:19)
49. "But as the days of ____ were, so shall also the coming of the Son of man be" (Matthew 24:37)

50. Telephoned
51. "For a good man some would even ____ to die" (Romans 5:7)
52. Acted
53. At loose ____
54. "We have seen his ____ in the east" (Matthew 2:2)

DOWN

1. Ship's record
2. Boyfriend for Babette?
3. N.T. book
4. Son of Gad (Genesis 46:16)
5. Share equally
6. In the manner of
7. "Render therefore unto ____" (Matthew 22:21)
8. "And by him all that believe are ____ from all things, from which ye could not be...by the law of Moses" (Acts 13:39)
9. Continent
10. Sound an alarm
13. Akin to a ringmaster (abbr.)
16. Individual number, for ATMs and credit cards
20. City in southern Judah (Joshua 15:50)
21. Bell bottoms or hula-hoops
22. Healing plant
23. "And let thy name be ____ for ever" (2 Samuel 7:26)
24. Hwy.
26. "Stand still, and ____ the salvation of the Lord" (Exodus 14:13)
27. Sea eagle
29. Formed a lap
30. Small town street name
32. Poetic contraction
34. "Take heed, ____ of the leaven of the Pharisees" (Mark 8:15)

37. "Oh that I had ____ like a dove!" (Psalm 55:6)
38. Required H.S. math
39. Obligations
40. Author Ayn
41. "____, lama sabachthani?" (Mark 15:34)
42. Ward off
45. Actor Johnson
46. Masculine nickname
47. Mouth (pl.)
48. Like a patio (abbr.)

ACROSS

1. Hand or season
4. "_____ things are lawful for me... but I will not be brought under the power" (1 Corinthians 6:12)
7. _____ the bill
11. Very (Fr.)
13. Medic's abbr.
14. King of Israel (1 Kings 16)
15. Bye-bye, to Brits
16. Canadian prov.
17. The act of (suffix)
18. Biblical measurement
19. "Redeem us from all iniquity, and purify unto himself a _____ people" (Titus 2:14)
21. Put on the feedbag
23. Pronoun
24. "They defile not their _____, in the midst whereof I dwell" (Numbers 5:3)
27. "For the _____ of this people cause them to err" (Isaiah 9:16)
32. To braid
33. "And the anger of the Lord was _____ against Israel" (Judges 2:20)
34. Great Lake
35. "Send me also cedar trees, fir trees...out of _____" (2 Chronicles 2:8)
37. Land measure (pl.)
38. That hurts!
39. Boring tool?
40. "_____ now thy Creator in the days of thy youth" (Ecclesiastes 12:1)
45. "Neither do the _____ understand judgment" (Job 32:9)
49. Great-grandfather of Lamech (Genesis 4:18)
50. Within (prefix)
51. Partner of rant
52. Virginia _____, first English child born in America
53. Possessive pronoun
54. Tied
55. Father of Ahira (Numbers 2:29)
56. Article
57. Golfer Ernie

DOWN

1. King of Germany, and Holy Roman Emperor
2. Oil filter maker
3. Honor, as at a banquet
4. Use as one's own
5. Single
6. "Nor the _____ of their shoes be broken" (Isaiah 5:27)
7. Young farm animal
8. All, everywhere (comb. form)
9. Killer whale
10. Arena area
12. "Unto none of them was Elias sent, save unto _____, a city of Sidon" (Luke 4:26)
20. Vowel trio
22. Simile syntax
24. Army rank (abbr.)
25. _____ wife
26. Fairy queen of English folklore
27. Actor Chaney
28. "Sing praises to the Lord..._____ among the people his doings" (Psalm 9:11)
29. Mess up
30. Bible grain (Isaiah 28:25)
31. French possessive pronoun
33. Nevertheless (arch.)
36. _____ de plume
37. Exclamation of protest
39. Was resurrected, as Jesus Christ

40. To stay afloat, with "out"
41. One of the sons of Shuthelah (Numbers 26:36)
42. "Call me ___: for the Almighty hath dealt very bitterly with me" (Ruth 1:20)
43. Idyllic setting
44. O.T. book
46. Contributed
47. First name in "daredeviltry"
48. Cubs' "cribs"?

BIBLE
Crosswords
Collection #12

Evelyn Boyington

Edited by
Ellen W. Caughey

BARBOUR
PUBLISHING, INC.
Uhrichsville, Ohio

Published by Barbour Publishing, Inc., P.O. Box 719, Uhrichsville, Ohio 44683
http://www.barbourbooks.com

Member of the
Evangelical Christian
Publishers Association

PUZZLE 1

ACROSS

1. KJV verb
5. Mouthfuls of chewing gum
9. Linking verb
12. Tribe of Israel
    (var., N.T. spelling)
13. Son of Rehoboam
    (1 Chronicles 3:10)
14. Body of water, in Boulogne
15. "Can any understand the ____ of
    the clouds?" (Job 36:29)
18. Note on the diatonic scale
19. Parched
20. Diminutive ending (pl.)
22. "The Lord is thy ____ upon thy
    right hand" (Psalm 121:5)
5. Printer's measure
    Of flying (prefix)
28. "The lot is cast into the ____"
    (Proverbs 16:33)
29. Misplace
31. Subject of Kilmer poem
33. "That through your mercy they
    also may ____ mercy"
    (Romans 11:31)
35. Boat ends
37. "The ____ of God is eternal life"
    (Romans 6:23)
38. It can be cold and hard
40. When Columbus is feted (abbr.)
41. Stagger
43. "____ with thine adversary
    quickly" (Matthew 5:25)
45. "They could not drink of the
    waters of ____" (Exodus 15:23)
46. "It is a ____ thing that the king
    requireth" (Daniel 2:11)
48. Workout zone (sing.)
49. The act of washing out or
    flushing
54. Crafty

56. Roof edge
57. ____ Bator (Mongolian capital)
58. Three (comb. form)
59. Lea languishers
60. Part of la famille

DOWN

1. Used to be
2. "The child shall play on the hole
   of the ____" (Isaiah 11:8)
3. Sunday speech (abbr.)
4. "I give unto you power to ____
   on scorpions" (Luke 10:19)
5. Dry valley or ravine, except in
   the rainy season
6. "The one who says he ____ in
   Him ought himself to walk in the
   same manner as He walked"
   (1 John 2:6, NAS)
7. Loud, continuous noise
8. Wise man
9. "I ____ he that liveth"
   (Revelation 1:18)
10. Adjunct to a resume
11. Historical periods
16. Son of Gad (Genesis 46:16)
17. Aver
21. "Thou shalt not be afraid for the
    ____ by night" (Psalm 91:5)
22. Trudge
23. In move-in condition
24. "All that were strong and ____
    ____ [2 words] war"
    (2 Kings 24:16)
26. Promontory; headland
30. Fairy-tale beginning
32. This (Sp.)
34. Grandson of Sheshan
    (1 Chronicles 2:35)
36. Father of Abraham
    (Luke 3:34)

39. Realize success
42. Number of months baby Moses was hidden before his mother put him in an ark (Exodus 2:2)
44. Elaborate dress
45. "Thou shalt be...as he that lieth upon the top of a ____" (Proverbs 23:34)
47. Matures
50. Not polished
51. ____ de la Cite, in Paris
52. "All that handle the ____, the mariners" (Ezekiel 27:29)
53. Compass dir.
55. Part of a century (abbr.)

PUZZLE 2

ACROSS

1. "I will come in to him and will ____ with him" (Revelation 3:20)
4. "The foxes have ____" (Matthew 8:20)
9. Isaac, to Abraham
12. ____-la-la
13. Pole vault or high jump, for example, in a track meet
14. "____ of every sort shalt thou bring into the ark" (Genesis 6:19)
15. Went in
17. Alter, hopefully for the better
19. "And he shall rule them with a rod of ____" (Revelation 2:27)
20. Celestial sign, to Magi
21. Remnant of a broken pot (KJV var.)
23. "Nor silver, nor brass...nor scrip for your ____" (Matthew 10:9, 10)
26. Fowl creatures
27. Nonsense
28. In ____ (concerning)
29. Consume
30. Certain collectibles
31. Age
32. Title used when not on a first-name basis (abbr.)
33. "You're So ____" (C. Simon hit)
34. Confirm
35. "If any man ____, let him come unto me" (John 7:37)
37. Drops pounds
38. Act as accomplice
39. Actor Orson, for one
40. "Ye are not in darkness, that that day should overtake you as a ____" (1 Thessalonians 5:4)
42. Pasture activity
45. Rowing implement
46. Chief son of Kohath (1 Chronicles 15:5)
48. Born (Fr.)
49. Twisted strand in rope
50. "Make a joyful noise unto the Lord, all ye ____" (Psalm 100:1)
51. Came into possession

DOWN

1. Jeanne d'Arc, e.g.
2. Vase
3. "Rejoicing in hope, ____ in tribulation" (Romans 12:12)
4. "For ____ feared John, knowing that he was a just man" (Mark 6:20)
5. Appliance
6. "He was ____ as a sheep to the slaughter" (Acts 8:32)
7. Half an em
8. Icons, perhaps
9. Far from cracking a smile
10. Possess
11. "And Cain...dwelt in the land of ____ on the east of Eden" (Genesis 4:16)
16. Blunders
18. One betrothed to Joseph
20. In the near future
21. Son of Noah
22. "A merry ____ maketh a cheerful countenance" (Proverbs 15:13)
23. Elbow, for one
24. "Who concerning the truth have ____, saying that the resurrection is past" (2 Timothy 2:18)
25. "For I have laid upon thee the ____ of their iniquity" (Ezekiel 4:5)
27. Raise up
30. "Be ____ for nothing" (Philippians 4:6)

31. After dusk
33. Emotional reaction (colloq.)
34. Son of Jotham, king of Judah
    (2 Kings 16:1)
36. Hirsute
37. What the Lamb opens, in the
    Book of Revelation
39. Partner of born
40. Over the ___
41. Masculine nickname
42. Cotton ___
43. New (comb. form)
44. "___ thee behind me, Satan"
    (Matthew 16:23)
47. Chemical element (abbr.)

PUZZLE 3

ACROSS

1. Collected prose or poetry of a particular time period (abbr.)
4. TV newsman Sevareid
8. Egg _____ soup, Chinese classic
12. Epoch
13. Beginning of refreshing brand name that "spells" summer to kids
14. Land measure
15. Ancient musical instrument, mentioned in Isaiah 5:12
17. "The Lord God will come with a strong hand, and his _____ shall rule" (Isaiah 40:10)
19. Where Sherman marched (abbr.)
20. "There is a _____ here, which hath five barley loaves" (John 6:9)
21. El ___
22. Deface
23. "Children, _____ your parents in the Lord" (Ephesians 6:1)
25. Sports venue
26. Prohibits
27. "Cast the _____ on the right side of
the ship" (John 21:6)
28. Total
29. _____ Auerbach, famed NBA coach
30. Masculine nickname
31. "Praise him with the _____ and dance" (Psalm 150:4)
33. Continent (abbr.)
35. "Take, _____: this is my body" (1 Corinthians 11:24)
36. Fare poorly
37. Possessed
38. "I will sing a new _____ unto thee, O God" (Psalm 144:9)
40. Popular street name
41. "All things were _____ by him" (John 1:3)
42. "I am too _____ to have an husband" (Ruth 1:12)
43. "The word _____ God" (John 1:1)
44. Chum
45. Atlantic state (abbr.)
46. Broadcast
47. "One jot or one __ shall in no wise pass from the law" (Matthew 5:18)
50. At any time
52. "For _____ Christ pleased not himself" (Romans 15:3)
54. Corn serving
55. "We shall all stand before the judgment _____ of Christ" (Romans 14:10)
56. Feast fashionably
57. Hair to _____ for (salon slogan)

DOWN

1. Tennis call
2. Gershwin
3. Pill, perhaps
4. Got by, barely, with "out"
5. Go bad
6. Vowel duo
7. _____ check
8. Hoover, for one
9. Cola brand name
10. Liver or lung, for example
11. Bosc and Anjou
16. Oz scarecrow Bolger
18. Byway (abbr.)
21. "They lifted up their voice with the trumpets and _____" (2 Chronicles 5:13)
22. Insane
23. United
24. "Rise, take up thy _____, and walk" (John 5:8)

25. Adhesive
26. _____ canto, singing style
28. Make a lap
29. Kin (abbr.)
31. Game where someone is "it"
32. "Over the _____" (goal of hoopsters)
33. "When ye fast, be not...of a _____ countenance" (Matthew 6:16)
34. Fruit drink
35. "The _____ of all things is at hand" (1 Peter 4:7)
37. Brought to a stop
38. "There was a certain beggar named Lazarus...full of _____" (Luke 16:20)
39. Item found in groves
40. Dog-_____ (like the pages of a book)
41. Tatami, commonly
43. Midwest state (abbr.)
44. Yearn for
46. "_____ thou the Christ?" (Luke 22:67)
47. Perfect score, to some
48. "I will both __ me down in peace, and sleep" (Psalm 4:8)
49. Poetic contraction
51. Apiece (abbr.)
53. Caribbean island group (abbr.)

PUZZLE 4

ACROSS

1. "I will go before thee, and...cut in sunder the ____ of iron" (Isaiah 45:2)
4. "For now we see through a ____, darkly" (1 Corinthians 13:12)
8. Optometrist's degree (abbr.)
10. "There followed ____ and fire mingled with blood" (Revelation 8:7)
12. "It is appointed unto men once to ____" (Hebrews 9:27)
13. One of twenty-six
14. Printer's measure
16. "____ for them that despitefully use you" (Matthew 5:44)
18. "They that sow in tears shall ____ in joy" (Psalm 126:5)
20. Slangy negative reply
22. First garden
24. "The nations are as a ____ of a bucket" (Isaiah 40:15)
26. Relative of 911
28. Was a pathfinder
30. "It is a people that do ____ in their heart" (Psalm 95:10)
31. Cream of the crop
32. Courtroom verb
34. Note in diatonic scale
35. "The ____ of mine apostleship are ye in the Lord" (1 Corinthians 9:2)
37. "Who is this that cometh from Edom, with ____ garments?" (Isaiah 63:1)
39. Simile syntax
41. "Let them learn first to shew ____ at home" (1 Timothy 5:4)
43. "Father, glorify thy ____" (John 12:28)
45. Sault ____ Marie

47. Chafed, as skin
48. Feminine nickname
49. Tattled, with "on"
51. Become bored
54. Cave dweller
56. Presummertime priority
58. Partner of dear
60. Dr. ____ (I. Fleming work)
61. Land-grant college department (abbr.)
62. Hula-Hoop, for one
64. Epochs
66. Western state (abbr.)
67. "____ yourselves unto God, as those that are alive from the dead" (Romans 6:13)
68. Created

DOWN

1. "____ there, done that"
2. Blood factor
3. "The trees of the Lord are full of ____" (Psalm 104:16)
4. Bag or rags
5. Classified, for one
6. Title of address
7. "He that goeth forth and weepeth, bearing precious ____, shall doubtless come again" (Psalm 126:6)
8. Send home
9. Beast of burden
11. Anger
15. Win by a ___
17. Give a holler
19. Linking verb
21. Coin ___
23. "Open thy hand wide unto...thy ____" (Deuteronomy 15:11)
25. Conceit
27. "There is but a ____ between me and death" (1 Samuel 20:3)

29. "A _____ in thy courts is better than a thousand" (Psalm 84:10)
31. "Every _____ of the forest is mine" (Psalm 50:10)
32. Fold
33. Cubs' coves
36. Tune, melody
38. To coat with slime and pitch, as Moses' mother did with his ark (Exodus 2:3)
40. Uninteresting
42. Jacob, to Esau
44. "A Jew of Tarsus... a citizen of no _____ city" (Acts 21:39)
46. Father of Hophni and Phineas

50. "The Philistine said, I _____ the armies of Israel" (1 Samuel 17:10)
52. "A bruised _____ shall he not break" (Isaiah 42:3)
53. "Incline thine __ unto me and hear my speech" (Psalm 17:6)
55. Sped like the wind
57. _____ chi, ancient Asian art of controlled exercise
59. What Abraham saw caught in a thicket (Genesis 22)
61. Exclamation of disappointment
63. Bethany Beach state (abbr.)
65. Continent (abbr.)

PUZZLE 5

ACROSS

1. "But the very ____ of your head are all numbered" (Matthew 10:30)
6. Throws a fit
11. Twilight
12. Changes the subject
14. California time (abbr.)
15. "Carry neither ____, nor scrip, nor shoes" (Luke 10:4)
17. A tree's blood
18. Buckeye bailiwick (abbr.)
19. "Prove me now...if I will not...____ you out a blessing" (Malachi 3:10)
20. Note on the diatonic scale
21. "____ it, even to the foundation thereof" (Psalm 137:7)
24. "Go, sell the ____ and pay thy debt" (2 Kings 4:7)
25. One of Jezebel's gods
27. "The stone shall cry out...and the beam out of the ____ shall answer it" (Habakkuk 2:11)
29. "And I was afraid, and went and hid thy ____ in the earth" (Matthew 25:25)
31. Long, long time
32. Thing, in legalese
33. Positions
36. Getaway destination
39. Adjective or adverb that is the equivalent of an exclamation mark
40. Take advantage of
42. Incite, with "on"
43. Printer's measure
44. A transparent body used to refract light
46. Quadrant in D.C.
47. Conjunction
49. Eagle abode
50. "There was no room for them in the ____" (Luke 2:7)
51. Escargots
53. "David ____ before the Lord with all his might" (2 Samuel 6:14)
55. Touching, as a gesture
56. Member of church hierarchy

DOWN

1. Friend of David (2 Samuel 15:32)
2. "Go to the ____, thou sluggard" (Proverbs 6:6)
3. Linking verb
4. Agent, slangily
5. Kin to comatose state
6. Outcome
7. To declare positively
8. Peachy place (abbr.)
9. Manuscript refiners (abbr.)
10. One who takes to the seas
11. "Be a ____!"
13. "We...are as water ____ on the ground" (2 Samuel 14:14)
16. Like Louis XIV, *par exemple*
22. Libel, slang
23. Pioneer African American periodical
25. "My soul may ____ thee before I die" (Genesis 27:4)
26. Fabled author
28. "Be sober, and hope to the ____ for the grace" (1 Peter 1:13)
30. Linking verb
33. In Sverige, you may meet more than a few
34. "Two ____ shall there be in one board" (Exodus 26:17)
35. Most certain
36. Hang one's hat
37. Messenger

38. Fashion statement
41. Title of respect
44. "Behold a ____ horse: and his
    name...was Death"
    (Revelation 6:8)
45. ____ ticket
48. Uncooked
50. Diamonds, slang
52. Oft-used abbr.
54. Bismarck bailiwick (abbr.)

ACROSS

1. "____ no man any thing, but to love one another" (Romans 13:8)
4. "His enemy came and sowed tares among the ____" (Matthew 13:25)
9. Greek letter
12. Benign skin tumor
13. "Let your laughter be turned to mourning, and your joy to ____" (James 4:9)
15. United ____
17. "Woe to them that are at ____ in Zion" (Amos 6:1)
18. Actor Buttons
19. "Ye shall no more give the people ____ to make brick" (Exodus 5:7)
22. Lets go
24. Article
25. Explorer Johnson
28. Preposition
29. Warns, ominously
31. Exclamations of disappointment
32. "Another angel came...having a golden ____" (Revelation 8:3)
34. Rouses, sometimes repeatedly
36. Entertaining troops is org.'s forte
37. One or the other
39. Half an em
40. Compass pt.
41. By means of
42. Acclaimed TV miniseries
44. Religion that has a claim in Jerusalem
46. Tribe of Israel
47. *My Name Is* ____ (W. Saroyan novel)
50. "He shall give thee the ____ of thine heart" (Psalm 37:4)
53. Those who trust in the Lord find this (Proverbs 16:20)

56. Continent (abbr.)
57. One that builds hills
58. "Shall I go and call to thee a ____ of the Hebrew women?" (Exodus 2:7)
59. Within (prefix)

DOWN

1. "His ____ received him not" (John 1:11)
2. "Much study is a ____ of the flesh" (Ecclesiastes 12:12)
3. "____ into his gates with thanksgiving" (Psalm 100:4)
4. Reporter's question
5. Brooding bunch
6. ____ *of Eden* (J. Steinbeck novel)
7. Madison, for one (abbr.)
8. Note on the diatonic scale
9. Orange pekoe, for one
10. "With the jaw of an ____...have I slain a thousand men" (Judges 15:16)
11. "He shall be a vessel...meet for the master's ____" (2 Timothy 2:21)
14. "What thing is this? what ____ doctrine is this?" (Mark 1:27)
16. Creative impulses
20. Where Saul abode: in Gibeah under a tree in ____ (1 Samuel 22:6)
21. Solution
22. Zero in on
23. Gets some shut-eye
25. "An angel of the Lord...sat under an ____" (Judges 6:11)
26. "This roll...was in my mouth as honey for ____" (Ezekiel 3:3)
27. Organizations (abbr.)

30. Israeli politician Sharon
33. Not "in a little while"
35. Son of Gad (Genesis 46:16)
38. _____ Vic's (former restaurant chain)
43. Rower
44. Mischievous one
45. Army repast
47. Exclamation of discovery
48. Bled, as madras might
49. Likely to
51. Compass pt.
52. _____ Paulo
54. Preposition
55. Greek letter

PUZZLE 7

ACROSS

1. Linking verb
4. Prophets, such as Samuel and Isaiah
9. Occupy; control
12. Suitable; apt
13. Doctrine or belief held as truth
14. Poetic before
15. "____ ____ ____ [3 words]; and blessed be my rock" (Psalm 18:46)
18. Status in a group, slang
19. Decay
20. Loiters or lingers (colloq.)
22. Gets ready to face the day
25. Exclamation of dismay
26. Referred to
28. Greek letter
29. Unit equal to 1/1,000 inch
30. "One load of bread, and one cake of ____ bread" (Exodus 29:23)
31. "If we say that we have no ____, we deceive ourselves" (1 John 1:8)
32. Fifth or Park, e.g.
33. "When thou prayest, ____ into thy closet" (Matthew 6:6)
34. Act stubbornly
35. Orderly
37. Puts aside
38. Option at car dealership
39. City near Bethel
40. "____ ____ ____ [3 words], O my soul. While I live will I praise" (Psalm 146:1, 2)
48. Owns
49. "The house was filled with the ____ of the ointment" (John 12:3)
50. Western Native American
51. Chemical ending
52. Memos
53. Button on the VCR (abbr.)

DOWN

1. "The servant of the Lord must...be...____ to teach" (2 Timothy 2:24)
2. Stadium sound
3. "The ____ God is thy refuge" (Deuteronomy 33:27)
4. Organ options
5. Poetic contraction
6. "Mark the perfect man...for the ____ of that man is peace" (Psalm 37:37)
7. Kin (abbr.)
8. "They ____ up the people, and the elders, and the scribes" (Acts 6:12)
9. Certain sports competitions
10. "Rabbi, thou ____ the Son of God" (John 1:49)
11. O.T. minor prophet (abbr.)
16. "The ____ of the lame are not equal" (Proverbs 26:7)
17. "The earth was without form, and ____" (Genesis 1:2)
20. In the Book of Esther, Mordecai's nemesis
21. "In Christ shall all be made ____" (1 Corinthians 15:22)
22. Son of Hezekiah (Ezra 2:16)
23. John on Patmos, for example
24. Is unable to swim
26. Bigger than a borough
27. Destination pour les vacances
30. "There was a dead man carried out, the ____ ____ [2 words] of his mother" (Luke 7:12)

31. "My spirit hath rejoiced in God my ____" (Luke 1:47)
33. Ornamental case
34. Idol of the Phoenicians and Tyrians
36. "Those that walk in pride he is able to ____" (Daniel 4:37)
40. Greek letter
41. Tore
42. Tokyo, formerly
43. Young one
44. Tint
45. Sounds of hesitation
46. Highway (abbr.)

47. "They shall wet thee with the ____ of heaven" (Daniel 4:25)

PUZZLE 8

ACROSS

1. Insect indicated in Deuteronomy 1:44
4. Clothes
8. Book division
12. Son of Abijam and good king of Judah
13. Medicinal plant
14. One of David's valiant men: ____ the Ahohite (1 Chronicles 11:29)
15. Affirmative
16. Blue or White
17. Sets goals
18. "For he is Lord of lords, and ____ ____ ____ [3 words]" (Revelation 17:14)
21. Members of conger family
22. "His bones are like bars of ____" (Job 40:18)
23. Debris
25. African antelope
26. Apiece (abbr.)
28. "The ____ are a people not strong" (Proverbs 30:25)
29. Child's play
30. Fine-feathered filler
32. Empire state (abbr.)
33. Reporter's question
34. Pulled along
35. "The day dawn, and the day ____ arise in your hearts" (2 Peter 1:19)
37. Horse or brake
38. Powerful acclamation of Jesus [3 words] (1 Timothy 6)
41. Add to the payroll
42. Father of Amos (Luke 3:25)
43. Shanty
45. Before (prefix)
46. Priest who "brought the law" (Nehemiah 8)
47. Wrath
48. Postparty scene
49. Quadrant of D.C.
50. "Be strong, and quit yourselves like ____" (1 Samuel 4:9)

DOWN

1. Hudson, for one
2. "He called the name of the well ____; because they strove with him" (Genesis 26:20)
3. Most direct, as a route
4. To make a knot
5. Medleys
6. Volkswagen vehicle
7. "I come ____ fruit on this fig tree, and find none" (Luke 13:7)
8. ____forte
9. Straighten, as a column
10. Drives into
11. Poetic contraction
19. New Jersey pros
20. Son of Caleb (1 Chronicles 4:15)
23. Pale
24. "If ____ of you lack wisdom, let him ask of God" (James 1:5)
25. Enola ____
26. Nathan told David the story of the ____ lamb
27. Conjunction
29. "By him were all things created... whether they be ____, or dominions" (Colossians 1:16)
30. "Behold, the judge standeth before the ____" (James 5:9)
31. "One was brought unto him, which ____ ____ [2 words] ten thousand talents" (Matthew 18:24)
33. Lump sum
34. Doubting disciple

35. Sifts, like socks
36. Ash, and others
37. Disparaging remark
38. "Their _____ is gone out through all the earth" (Psalm 19:4)
39. Bother
40. "Be ye _____ of this, that the kingdom of God is come nigh unto you" (Luke 10:11)
41. Son of Noah
44. "Your father hath deceived me, and changed my wages _____ times" (Genesis 31:7)

ACROSS

1. Deface
4. A seal or official stamp
8. Like a black pearl
12. Poetic before
13. Aesop's foolish fellow
14. Great Lake
15. Masculine nickname
16. Son of Jerahmeel
    (1 Chronicles 2:25)
17. Darius the ____, one-time ruler
    of Babylon
18. Far ___
20. Bane of insomniacs (pl.)
22. Grammar-school essay
24. Liquid measure
25. "They may teach the young ____
    to be sober" (Titus 2:4)
26. Sheltered side
27. FBI agent, familiarly
30. Symbolic sign
31. Owns
32. Harsh breathing
33. Meditation by preacher (abbr.)
34. "My house shall be called the
    house of prayer; but ye have
    made it a ____ of thieves"
    (Matthew 21:13)
35. "Thou shalt not bear ____
    witness" (Exodus 20:16)
36. Trench surrounding fortified place
37. "So I sware in my wrath, They
    shall not ____ into my rest"
    (Hebrews 3:11)
38. "Except ye ____, ye shall all
    likewise perish" (Luke 13:3)
41. Make a judgment
42. "The fire shall ____ be burning
    upon the altar" (Leviticus 6:13)
43. "Father, save me from this
    ____" (John 12:27)
45. River or Sea
48. Close by
49. Ultimatum word
50. Blunder
51. "I beseech thee, look upon my
    son: for he is mine ____ child"
    (Luke 9:38)
52. "For ye have ____ of patience"
    (Hebrews 10:36)
53. Actress Laraine

DOWN

1. "They...found the colt tied by the
   door...where two ways ____"
   (Mark 11:4)
2. Linking verb
3. "I know that my ____ liveth"
   (Job 19:25)
4. "A good name is rather to be
   ____ than great riches"
   (Proverbs 22:1)
5. "Then shall the lame man leap as
   an ____" (Isaiah 35:6)
6. Mine find
7. Common cents
8. Forgive or pardon
9. Greek god of war
10. Let it ___
11. Shoe sizes
19. "For all the promises of God in
    him are yea, and in him ____"
    (2 Corinthians 1:20)
21. "One thousand shall flee at the
    rebuke of ____" (Isaiah 30:17)
22. Jesus sent His disciples out by
    ____ (Mark 6:7)
23. Base in baseball
24. "They shall ____ vineyards, but
    not drink the wine thereof"
    (Zephaniah 1:13)
27. Wavered

28. In addition
29. *The _____ Slayer* (J. F. Cooper novel)
31. "The idols of the _____ are silver and gold" (Psalm 135:15)
32. Throw a fit
34. Puzo's Corleone
35. "The Lord...is to be _____ above all gods" (1 Chronicles 16:25)
36. "A _____ heart maketh a cheerful countenance" (Proverbs 15:13)
38. First woman to be U.S. Attorney General
39. "Let me be weighed in an _____ balance" (Job 31:6)
40. Ring out
41. Masquerade of sorts
44. Corrida cry
46. Age
47. "He turneth...the watersprings into _____ ground" (Psalm 107:33)

ACROSS

1. "Except I shall see in his hands the print of the ____" (John 20:25)
6. "Bring forth...every living thing...that they may ____ abundantly" (Genesis 8:17)
11. "Take heed and beware of the ____ of the Pharisees" (Matthew 16:6)
12. Occupied an apartment
14. More than a kernel
15. Wife of Abram
17. Tavern brew
18. Mideast dialect (abbr.)
19. "____ up a child in the way he should go" (Proverbs 22:6)
20. Buffalo college
21. "The ____ of the temple was rent in twain" (Matthew 27:51)
24. "This gospel...shall be preached in all the world...and then shall the ____ come" (Matthew 24:14)
25. 1,061, to Claudius
27. Bloopers
29. "Ye shall appoint you cities...of refuge...that the ____ may flee thither" (Numbers 35:11)
31. Cereal grain
32. Son of Bela (Numbers 26:40)
33. Grouped together
36. Claudius ____, who wrote a letter to Felix on Paul's behalf (Acts 23:26)
39. ____ is more
40. The Gilded Age, for one
42. Say "whoa"
43. Printer's measure
44. Shasta ____
46. Hawkeye state (abbr.)
47. Red, for one
49. "I am ____ and Omega" (Revelation 22:13)
50. Put it in writing
51. English or western, in the tack room
53. Item to do
55. "The angels shall come forth, and ____ the wicked from among the just" (Matthew 13:49)
56. Tizzies

DOWN

1. "Now is our salvation ____ than when we believed" (Romans 13:11)
2. Rhine tributary
3. Patient adjunct, in hospital (abbr.)
4. For fear that
5. "But they [other nations] shall be ____ and traps unto you" (Joshua 23:13)
6. "French" is one style of these
7. Slow down or stop
8. Fourteenth letter of the alphabet
9. Greek letter
10. Super-duper
11. "For thou wilt not ____ my soul in hell" (Psalm 16:10)
13. King of Eglon (Joshua 10:3)
16. Headed for the hills
22. Golfer's gear
23. Large quantities
25. Mystery writer Ngaio
26. Seller of purple from Thyatira
28. Highway (abbr.)
30. "Now I ____ me down..."
33. "I will ____ thy name for ever and ever" (Psalm 145:1)
34. Man sick with the palsy for eight years (Acts 9)
35. Wheeler follower

36. Speaks angrily, with "out"
37. Not citizens
38. "Put on the whole armour of God, that ye may be able to _____ against the wiles of the devil" (Ephesians 6:11)
41. Tear
44. Roy's partner
45. Storyteller's specialty
48. Summer drink
50. Almost too reasonable, as an excuse
52. Wounded ex-soldier (abbr.)
54. Eastern U.S. state

PUZZLE 11

ACROSS

1. Linking verb
4. Makes like the sun
9. Possesses
12. Insane
13. Lovable nerd on TV's "Family Matters"
14. Honest one
15. French conjunction
16. Land from which the Lord will recover the remnant of His people (Isaiah 11:11)
18. Live for the moment
19. Like food and clothing
21. Held with a certain tool
23. Frost, for one
25. Pitch in
26. High priest in Shiloh
28. More reliable
30. Director Lupino
33. Poetic contraction
34. "Then ____ brought out silver and gold out of the treasures of the house of the Lord" (2 Chronicles 16:2)
35. Spat
36. Likely
37. TV's "Get ___"
39. Frozen water
40. "Thy word is a ____ unto my feet" (Psalm 119:105)
42. "And he...cast him into prison, till he should pay the ____" (Matthew 18:30)
44. At a certain location
46. Organic substance from plants
49. Concerning
50. "While the bridegroom ____ they all slumbered and slept" (Matthew 25:5)
54. Therefore
55. Vein contents
57. What hobos rode
58. In the manner of
59. Benign skin tumor
60. Lacking originality
61. O.T. book (abbr.)

DOWN

1. So be it
2. Per diem, for one
3. Before PCs, one who used a blue pencil (abbr.)
4. Particular potato
5. April correspondent (abbr.)
6. TV's "____ King"
7. Poetic contraction
8. Splinter
9. Half a laugh
10. French cleric
11. "He that goeth forth and weepeth, bearing precious ____" (Psalm 126:6)
16. "Why make ye this ____, and weep?" (Mark 5:39)
17. To pain, discomfort, or trouble
20. Letter from Paul
22. "Who maketh his angels ____; his ministers a flaming fire" (Psalm 104:4)
24. Trudge along
25. "I cannot hold my peace, because thou hast ____, O my soul, the sound of the trumpet" (Jeremiah 4:19)
26. Greek letter
27. ____ service
29. Team ____, e.g., at the Olympics
31. Halliday, for one
32. Reverence
37. Rips one's reputation

38. Feminine name (var.)
41. Masculine nickname
43. "Arise, take up thy ____, and go unto thine house" (Matthew 9:6)
44. Believe or think (arch.)
45. In or at this place
47. Man, for one
48. Father of Japheth
51. Tell on
52. Inlet
53. Feeling poorly
56. ___-Gedi, city of Judah (Joshua 15)
58. Article

PUZZLE 12

ACROSS

1. When a rooster rouses
5. Air (comb. form)
8. A. Hitchcock film classic
12. Operatic solo
13. Busy one
14. First garden
15. Tree house
16. Under the weather
17. Center
18. Was wary, with "away"
20. "When ye blow an ____, then the camps...on the east shall go forward" (Numbers 10:5)
22. "But ____ thing is needful: and Mary hath chosen" (Luke 10:42)
23. Jesus likens the kingdom of God to ____ virgins (Matthew 25)
24. Makes payment for, as Jesus' sacrifice on the cross
27. "And as they were ____, Jesus took bread" (Matthew 26:26)
31. "A brother offended is harder to be ____ than a strong city" (Proverbs 18:19)
32. ___classical style
33. Let go
37. Saul's exit "vehicle" out of Damascus (Acts 9)
40. Body part of priest on which the ram's blood was sprinkled (Exodus 29:20)
41. Employ
42. Times to "catch the worm"
44. Experienced labored breathing
47. Experience ennui
48. Where the good Samaritan left the wounded man
50. Lions' den
52. Sheltered side, nautically
53. "Deliver thyself as a ____ from the hand of the hunter" (Proverbs 6:5)
54. Firstborn of Isaac
55. Held or kept in, with "up"
56. "Be sober, and hope to the ____ for the grace" (1 Peter 1:13)
57. Niece and nephew, e.g. (abbr.)

DOWN

1. Tribe of Israel
2. Greek counterpart of Mars
3. "Let them be...put to shame that ____ me evil" (Psalm 40:14)
4. "Let us cut it [Moab] off from being a ____" (Jeremiah 48:2)
5. Awaits; stays close to
6. Conger
7. Feel a kinship toward
8. Retract
9. Aroma
10. Salon service
11. Chemical suffix
19. Compass dir.
21. Grassy field
24. A piercing tool
25. "Is any thing ____ hard for the Lord?" (Genesis 18:14)
26. "The sons of...Shamed, who built ____, and Lod" (1 Chronicles 8:12)
28. "He pronounced all these words...and I wrote them with ____ in the book" (Jeremiah 36:18)
29. Born (Fr.)
30. Purchased
34. Mulberry, for one
35. Ages and ages
36. "I ____ to be present with you now" (Galatians 4:20)

37. "The bush_____ with fire, and the bush was not consumed" (Exodus 3:2)
38. Good king of Judah
39. Lydia was a _____ of purple
42. Burrowing mammal
43. "_____ me first" (former Kodak come-on)
45. "His soul shall dwell at _____" (Psalm 25:13)
46. _____ tone
47. Cartographer's product
49. Forget it, to Philippe
51. Masculine nickname (var.)

PUZZLE 13

ACROSS

1. Director Peckinpah
4. Understands
8. "Thou liftest me up to the wind; thou causest me to ____ upon it" (Job 30:22)
12. Ripen
13. Secular person
14. SW Ohio city
15. "Blessed be the God and ____ of our Lord Jesus Christ" (1 Peter 1:3)
17. "Whosoever shall exalt himself shall be ____" (Matthew 23:12)
19. "I ____ not from thy precepts" (Psalm 119:110)
20. "Let us run with patience the ____ that is set before us" (Hebrews 12:1)
21. "To do" tasks
24. Crone
27. So much, so great
29. New Jersey, to Noelle
31. ____ shirt
32. Dolly's domain (abbr.)
33. "We should be holy and without ____ before him in love" (Ephesians 1:4)
34. Administrator of TLC
35. Fruity drink
37. To be (Fr.)
38. University of Michigan's Schembeckler, familiarly
40. "He [Judah] couched as a lion... who shall ____ him up?" (Genesis 49:9)
42. Where Saul encountered a witch
44. Son of Melchi (Luke 3:27)
46. Blot out

49. "The Lord said, My ____ shall not always strive with man" (Genesis 6:3)
51. Does the hora
52. Act or result (suffix)
53. "____ was a tiller of the ground" (Genesis 4:2)
55. Meadow
56. Masculine nickname
57. Disapproving sound
58. Flightless bird

DOWN

1. "The king said, Is the young man Absalom ___?" (2 Samuel 18:29)
2. "For this ____ is mount Sinai in Arabia" (Galatians 4:25)
3. ____ system
4. Animal not to be eaten (Deuteronomy 14:13)
5. It contains a hammer and a stirrup
6. Note on diatonic scale
7. To mark permanently
8. "Then saith he to Thomas, ____ hither thy finger" (John 20:27)
9. Place inside
10. Stag's mate
11. Bitter or dead
16. Abraham and Sarah were buried in field purchased from sons of ____ (Genesis 25)
18. Tend to a turkey
22. "The heart of Egypt shall ____ in the midst of it" (Isaiah 19:1)
23. "I may tell all my bones: they look and ____ upon me" (Psalm 22:17)

25. Poetic contraction
26. Benign tumors
27. "There fell a great____ from heaven" (Revelation 8:10)
28. Disentangle
30. "Let all the people say, ____" (Psalm 106:48)
33. Father of Hosea (Hosea 1:1)
36. Mother of Timothy (2 Timothy 1:5)
38. "Unto you is ____ this day...a Saviour" (Luke 2:11)
39. Kin to a prophet

41. Son of Zebulun (Genesis 46:14)
43. College officials
45. Restless desire
47. Appear likely
48. "____ despised his birthright" (Genesis 25:34)
49. Game, ____, match
50. Like an IOU, only more specific
51. Show no respect (colloq.)
54. "I have given into thy hand the king of ____, and his people" (Joshua 8:1)

PUZZLE 14

ACROSS

1. Places for the accident prone (abbr.)
4. Things to do
9. "Festus said...much learning doth make thee ____" (Acts 26:24)
12. "The trees of the Lord are full of ____" (Psalm 104:16)
13. First letter of Hebrew alphabet
14. Hullabaloo
15. "The Lord had prepared a great fish to ____ up Jonah" (Jonah 1:17)
17. Consumed
19. Noise or disturbance
20. "Have ____ in yourselves, and have peace one with another" (Mark 9:50)
21. Star of Gigi
23. "The ____ beguiled me, and I did eat" (Genesis 3:13)
26. In a short time (arch.)
27. Swift mammals
28. Conjunction
29. Girl Scouts of America founder
30. ____ girl
31. Actor Vigoda
32. Maxwell Perkins, to F.S. Fitzgerald (abbr.)
33. "For whosoever will ____ his life shall lose it" (Luke 9:24)
34. "I...am persuaded that he is ____ to keep that which I have committed" (2 Timothy 1:12)
35. Edible bugs, according to Leviticus 11:22
37. "The ____ of them which have reaped are entered into the ears of the Lord" (James 5:4)
38. Feminine nickname
39. House or hog

40. Motif
42. Old Testament book
45. "____ ____ [2 words] the Rose of Sharon" (Song of Solomon 2:1)
46. "The good shepherd giveth his life for the ____" (John 10:11)
48. Ascot, for one
49. Less than desirable abode
50. Certain amphibians
51. Stolen (colloq.)

DOWN

1. Type of curve
2. Unrefined
3. "Yea, the ____ hath found an house" (Psalm 84:3)
4. Bird claw
5. Oodles
6. "Woe to the women that ____ pillows to all armholes" (Ezekiel 13:18)
7. Mess duty (abbr.)
8. "Like a lamb dumb before his ____" (Acts 8:32)
9. Dull finish
10. Summer quaff
11. Actor Ameche
16. "The first beast was like a ____" (Revelation 4:7)
18. European mountain range
20. Dried up; withered
21. One of the twelve spies sent by Moses into Canaan (Numbers 13)
22. Positively charged electrode
23. Jesus ____ our souls
24. Duke or earl, for example
25. Isaiah describes these as clapping their hands
27. Shanty; hut
30. "Why ____ thou me good?" (Matthew 19:17)

31. "Like unto the Son of God; _____ a priest continually" (Hebrews 7:3)
33. "There shall come forth a rod out of the _____ of Jesse" (Isaiah 11:1)
34. Mideast resident
36. "How long shall mine _____ be exalted?" (Psalm 13:2)
37. Graduate degree tests (abbr.)
39. Regretted
40. Poetic contraction
41. _____ trick
42. Teachers' organization (abbr.)
43. _____ Grande
44. Jelled
47. "_____, every one that thirsteth" (Isaiah 55:1)

PUZZLE 15

ACROSS

1. "They came to the threshing-floor of ____, which is beyond Jordan" (Genesis 50:10)
5. Highway (abbr.)
8. Bargain events
10. ____ apple (candy flavor)
11. "After the same manner also he took the cup, when he had ____" (1 Corinthians 11:25)
13. Beyond compare
15. Paddle
16. Momentous sign
17. ___-Eglaim, near the Salt Sea (Ezekiel 47)
18. Wight, for one
19. *King* ____ (J. Clavell novell)
20. Went golfing
21. "The Lord is good to ____" (Psalm 145:9)
24. Compass dir.
25. Like some numbers
26. ____ bargain
27. "These shall ye not eat of them that chew the ____" (Leviticus 11:4)
28. Minor prophet
29. Conjunction
30. "For we are saved by ____" (Romans 8:24)
34. "He it is, to whom I shall give a ____, when I have dipped it" (John 13:26)
35. "They shall lay hands on the sick, and they shall ____" (Mark 16:18)
37. Entrapped
40. "So be it"
41. "When he had made a scourge... he ____ them all out of the temple" (John 2:15)
42. David ___-Gurion
43. Action

DOWN

1. Was in agreement
2. Greek letter
3. Mount Blanc is one
4. "He [Nebuchadnezzar] was ____ from his kingly throne" (Daniel 5:20)
5. Stronger than string
6. "Whosoever shall smite thee on thy right cheek, __ to him the other" (Matthew 5:39)
7. Poetic before
9. "Ye were ____ with that holy Spirit of promise" (Ephesians 1:13)
10. "How precious also are thy thoughts...how great is the ____ of them" (Psalm 139:17)
12. ____ Scott, subject of landmark legal case
13. Hence
14. Dry or liquid
18. Judge Lance
19. Taped
21. "I see a rod of an ____ tree" (Jeremiah 1:11)
22. "The ____ shall lie down with the kid" (Isaiah 11:6)
23. ____ Cruces, NM
26. Bridge response
30. "Whilst we are at ____ in the body, we are absent from the Lord" (2 Corinthians 5:6)
31. "God so clothe the grass... which to day is, and to morrow is cast into the ____" (Matthew 6:30)

32. "I will not with ink and _____
    write unto thee" (3 John 13)
33. Hesitation sound
36. NYC sight
38. "Let her be as the loving hind
    and the pleasant _____"
    (Proverbs 5:19)
39. First female

PUZZLE 16

ACROSS

1. "Will a man ____ God?" (Malachi 3:8)
4. Moon or mast
8. German physicist
11. Son of Seth (Genesis 4:26)
13. Bread spread
14. Dramatic feathery wrap
15. Israel seaport
16. "For thus saith the high and lofty One that inhabiteth ____" (Isaiah 57:15)
18. Time on the religious calendar
19. Note on the diatonic scale
20. Playwright's direction
24. "Is Israel a servant? is he a homeborn ____?" (Jeremiah 2:14)
28. Measure of journey
30. Small space
32. Jellylike substance
33. Son of Abijam; king of Judah
34. "And supper being ____, the devil having now put into the heart of Judas Iscariot" (John 13:2)
36. "Above the ____" (goal of b'ball players)
37. Yes, in Yokohama
38. Saline drop
39. Golfer Ernie
40. Like some egg yolks
43. ____ scheme
45. Many-tome resource (abbr.)
47. Ancient Hebrew dry measure
50. "Minister the same one to another, as good ____" (1 Peter 4:10)
55. Tractor-trailer, to many (colloq.)
56. Person who has to do with (suffix)
57. Protest, with "against"
58. Cut off
59. "He that hath a bountiful ____ shall be blessed" (Proverbs 22:9)
60. Hold ___
61. Three, in Turin

DOWN

1. Camino ___
2. "God hath spoken ___; twice have I heard this" (Psalm 62:11)
3. "Being ____ ____ [2 words], not of corruptible seed" (1 Peter 1:23)
4. Tend to the garden
5. Mountain measure (abbr.)
6. Beloved general of Virginia
7. Creates from nothing
8. Japanese sash
9. Like dog days
10. Feminine name
12. Complete collections
17. Nothing
21. "He casteth forth his ____ like morsels" (Psalm 147:17)
22. Impression
23. Pliny the ____ (Roman writer)
25. "And what ____ hath the temple of God with idols?" (2 Corinthians 6:16)
26. "And, behold, the ____ of the temple was rent in twain" (Matthew 27:51)
27. Shade trees
28. Wizard of Oz actor
29. "Jacob have I loved, but ____ have I hated" (Romans 9:13)
31. "Tender-eyed" woman of the Old Testament
35. Parched
41. Partner of then
42. "The ____ of the wicked shall be shortened" (Proverbs 10:27)

44. Playwright Hart
46. "No man can come to me, except the Father which hath sent me ____ him" (John 6:44)
48. Arab chieftain
49. "The harvest of the earth is ____" (Revelation 14:15)
50. "O taste and ____ that the Lord is good" (Psalm 34:8)
51. Mystery writer Josephine
52. Poetic before
53. Throughout; across (prefix)
54. Wily; conniving

PUZZLE 17

ACROSS

1. Spelunker's domain
5. "Out of his belly shall ____ rivers of living water" (John 7:38)
9. Majorette's must
10. "Ye are all children of ____" (1 Thessalonians 5:5)
12. Tendon
13. "I will come in to him, and will ____ with him" (Revelation 3:20)
14. At present
16. Chemical suffix
17. Off one's rocker
18. "There is none righteous, ____, not one" (Romans 3:10)
19. Biblical exclamation
20. ____ Western Reserve University
21. VCR button
23. "Lo, I am with you alway, even unto the ____ of the world" (Matthew 28:20)
25. Orthopedists' org., and many others (abbr.)
26. "They were swifter than eagles, they were stronger than ____" (2 Samuel 1:23)
27. Latest fad
29. "Yet ____ of you keepeth the law" (John 7:19)
30. Stock in trade
32. Family room, formerly
33. "A time to rend, and a time to ____" (Ecclesiastes 3:7)
36. Mammoth
37. Meat paste
38. Bar Harbor state (abbr.)
39. Preposition
40. "Dear ____:"
41. "____ up the gift of God, which is in thee" (2 Timothy 1:6)
43. Summer, en Paris
45. Coop denizen
46. For ____!
47. Ancestor of Jesus; father of Achim (Matthew 1:14)
49. Tows away
50. Cantered
51. "The coast turneth to Ramah, and to the strong city ____" (Joshua 19:29)

DOWN

1. Sugar, for one
2. Gobbled up
3. "____ , and pay unto the Lord your God" (Psalm 76:11)
4. Printer's measure
5. James Galway's forte
6. "My ____ shall utter praise" (Psalm 119:171)
7. King of Bashan (1 Kings 4:19)
8. *Pourquoi*, to Pete
9. Before the West was won, they were plentiful
11. Partner of mortise
12. White ___
13. Capital of ancient Elam, now a city in ruins in Iran
15. A-one
17. "Father, glorify thy ____" (John 12:28)
20. Canary coop
21. "For the wages of ____ is death" (Romans 6:23)
22. Appendages
24. Bore (colloq.)
26. Unattached
28. Linking verb
29. "They straightway left their ____, and followed him" (Matthew 4:20)

30. If the _____ fits....
31. Pursues with a vengeance
32. Mend a sock
34. "The _____ dwelt therein in times past, a people great" (Deuteronomy 2:10)
35. Existed
37. _____ de resistance
40. "Your feet _____ with the preparation of the gospel of peace" (Ephesians 6:15)
41. "Abraham journeyed...and dwelled between Kadesh and _____" (Genesis 20:1)
42. "We spend our years as a _____ that is told" (Psalm 90:9)
44. What the high priest's servant lost in the Garden of Gethsemane, temporarily
46. Have one's _____
48. "Let him eschew evil, and _____ good" (1 Peter 3:11)
49. Kin to alt.

PUZZLE 18

ACROSS

1. Have Midas' touch
5. "God is...a very present _____ in trouble" (Psalm 46:1)
9. Unit with several rooms (abbr.)
12. _____ code
13. State one's case
14. Certain princess' veggie villain
15. "When he had found one _____ of great price, went and sold all" (Matthew 13:46)
17. Debussy's "Le ___"
18. High school subject (abbr.)
19. Kind of gloves
21. Escalator alternative
23. Unlikely hit
27. Take-home pay
28. Between a rock and a hard place
29. Lion _____
31. "Unto whom he said, _____, such a one!" (Ruth 4:1)
33. Employ
34. Title in Tijuana
35. "Yet _____ is born unto trouble" (Job 5:7)
36. Exist
37. Kind of watercraft
38. What it's better to be
39. Fire
40. Defies detention
42. Tide, Crest, and others
45. Sympathetic sound
46. "Give _____ unto the law of our God" (Isaiah 1:10)
47. Detergent name
49. Purple peddler of Philippi
53. Linking verb
54. Den of beasts
56. Many, many moons (pl.)
57. Buttons or Auerbach
58. "Consider the lilies...they toil not, they _____ not" (Luke 12:27)
59. Descartes

DOWN

1. "Stand in the _____ before me for the land" (Ezekiel 22:30)
2. Anger
3. Idyllic setting
4. "I will _____ the earth in the clear day" (Amos 8:9)
5. Initials of electronics giant
6. Small-town America street
7. Actress Grant, and others
8. "Whoso is _____ with a thief hateth his own soul" (Proverbs 29:24)
9. Divide asunder, familiarly
10. On a ___
11. Vittles
16. Sass
20. Prevent
22. Air (comb. form)
23. Broadway souvenir
24. Don't win some
25. Poetic before
26. Songdom's "home"
30. One of the "3 Stooges," and others
31. "Do good to them which _____ you" (Luke 6:27)
32. Addition column
34. "But be shod with _____; and not put on two coats" (Mark 6:9)
35. It usually has a key
37. Prohibit
38. "And, behold, a certain _____ stood up and tempted him" (Luke 10:25)
39. Was concerned about
41. Masculine nickname

42. "In their hands they shall _____ thee up" (Matthew 4:6)
43. "It is a _____ thing that the king requireth" (Daniel 2:11)
44. Smite, more familiarly
48. Weeks in a year, Roman style
50. Stag's mate
51. Bed and breakfast, for example
52. Chemical suffix
55. Hospital employee (abbr.)

PUZZLE 19

ACROSS

1. Heavenly being (Fr.)
5. "____ gave names to all cattle" (Genesis 2:20)
9. Get equipped
12. "Who shall ____ us away the stone from the door of the sepulchre?" (Mark 16:3)
13. By the side of (prefix)
14. Talk baby talk
15. Made footprints
16. Arab chieftain
17. Classic auto
18. Looks at a book
20. Bureau
22. On the ____ day Jesus rose from the dead
24. Pronoun for an ocean liner
25. ____ Grande
26. Have a ___
29. Minor prophet
33. "So the wall was finished in the twenty and fifth day of the month ____" (Nehemiah 6:15)
35. Like henna
36. "Take also of the tree of life... and ____ forever" (Genesis 3:22)
37. "I am, and none ____ beside me" (Isaiah 47:8)
38. Ruby, and others
40. Born (Fr.)
41. "I took the little book...and ____ it up" (Revelation 10:10)
43. "For I know the thoughts that I ____ toward you" (Jeremiah 29:11)
45. Rhombus or rectangle, for example
48. Dashes off
50. Poetic contraction
51. Solo for Dame Sutherland
53. "They came to the threshing-floor of ____" (Genesis 50:10)
56. Force to be accepted
57. Sacrifice
58. Singer McIntire
59. "I the Lord search the heart, I ____ the reins" (Jeremiah 17:10)
60. Table d'____
61. High school course (abbr.)

DOWN

1. "Our Father which ____ in heaven" (Matthew 6:9)
2. Conjunction
3. "The light of the ____ gospel of Christ" (2 Corinthians 4:4)
4. "Rebuke not an ____, but entreat him as a father" (1 Timothy 5:1)
5. Mimicked
6. Hoover, and others
7. Exodus hero
8. The ____ sisters of Little Women
9. Seaport in Israel
10. European deer
11. ____ point
19. Classified material
21. "____ the sick, cleanse the lepers" (Matthew 10:8)
22. "I give to eat of the ____ of life" (Revelation 2:7)
23. "I set my king upon my holy ____ of Zion" (Psalm 2:6)
24. Flower part
27. Boundary
28. Popeye's short answer
30. "Thou shalt be a good ____ of Jesus Christ" (1 Timothy 4:6)
31. "The day cometh, that shall burn as an ____" (Malachi 4:1)
32. "____ ye first the kingdom of God" (Matthew 6:33)

34. _____ year
39. Female saint (Fr. abbr.)
42. "I will..._____ thee in the way which thou shalt go" (Psalm 32:8)
44. "The law of his God is in his _____" (Psalm 37:31)
45. Kind
46. Understand, in a way
47. Arnie's _____ (golfer's gallery)
48. Make a _____
49. With "of," recently
52. Milne marsupial
54. Daughter of Zachariah (2 Kings 18:2)

55. Hammarskjold, to friends

PUZZLE 20

ACROSS

1. ____ canto (singing style)
4. Queen of ____
9. "The ____ of the Lord is at hand" (Joel 1:15)
12. Mirror
13. Instrument board
14. "The wheat and the ____ were not smitten" (Exodus 9:32)
15. "Blessed is the man that walketh not...nor standeth in the way of ____" (Psalm 1:1)
17. "They that dwell in my house, and my ____, count me for a stranger" (Job 19:15)
19. Prong
20. "____ not sleep, lest thou come to poverty" (Proverbs 20:13)
21. Milk that doesn't require tears
23. "Isaac loved Esau, because he did eat of his ____" (Genesis 25:28)
26. Stubborn sort
27. Holds; restrains
28. One of the Kettles
29. Golfer Ernie
30. Alights
31. "And beneath upon the ____ of it [ephod] thou shalt make pomegranates of blue" (Exodus 28:33)
32. Simile syntax
33. Skin afflictions
34. Wise man
35. Shrinks
37. Fathers, familiarly
38. Burden
39. ___meet (a spouse)
40. Onionlike vegetables
42. "I will ____ the lovingkindnesses of the Lord" (Isaiah 63:7)
45. Reply (abbr.)
46. "____ up a child in the way he should go" (Proverbs 22:6)
48. Before
49. Understand, really
50. Popular Parker Bros. game
51. Saw ___

DOWN

1. ____-relief (sculpture technique)
2. Upon; over (prefix)
3. Old World legumes
4. Exhausted
5. Rabbit's relative
6. Naval rank (abbr.)
7. Exist
8. What Aaron's rod yielded (Numbers 17)
9. Takes away moisture
10. First ___
11. Affirmative
16. Blue or White
18. Hertz competitor
20. Loans money
21. Smudge
22. ____ rate
23. Climbing vegetation
24. Greek letter
25. "Rather rejoice, because your ____ are written in heaven" (Luke 10:20)
27. Reveals, as one's soul
30. "His meat was ____ and wild honey" (Matthew 3:4)
31. More satisfied
33. "The stone ____ into his forehead" (1 Samuel 17:49)
34. "Let your speech be alway with grace, seasoned with ____" (Colossians 4:6)
36. KJV verb

37. "He had agreed with the labourers for a _____ a day" (Matthew 20:2)
39. Bequeathed one
40. Fall behind
41. Compass dir.
42. Scratch or stain, for example
43. It runs in veins
44. Masculine nickname
47. Right-hand page (abbr.)

PUZZLE 21

ACROSS

1. "Sing unto him, sing ____ unto him" (1 Chronicles 16:9)
7. Father of Abraham (Luke 3:34)
12. Hangs one's hat
14. Has a fit
15. Mount. measure
16. "When even was come, he ____ down with the twelve" (Matthew 26:20)
17. Nicklaus's needs
18. "You've got ____" (computer memo)
20. "I have ____ thee with an everlasting love" (Jeremiah 31:3)
22. Atlantic state (abbr.)
23. One who requires taming
25. Cast out
26. "These ____ times have ye reproached me" (Job 19:3)
27. "They call their lands after their own ____" (Psalm 49:11)
29. Gossip (colloq.)
30. San ____, NM
32. "Manasseh...hath made Judah also to sin with his ____" (2 Kings 21:11)
34. "____ tu": how Juan would say, "It's you."
35. Loose
37. French seasoning
38. Before (prefix)
39. Tribe of Israel
43. Energy unit (abbr.)
44. Rector's residence
46. Raconteur's revelation
47. Dromedary, to Bismarck
49. Nicotine's no-good partner
51. Chemical suffix
52. Emulate Daniel Webster
53. Moved, emotionally
55. What Naaman was (2 Kings 5:1)
56. "Owls shall dwell there, and ____ shall dance there" (Isaiah 13:21)

DOWN

1. Hyde Park sight (pl.)
2. Hebrew term, found in Psalms
3. Just waking up
4. Chinese measure of distance
5. AMA members
6. "Shut up the words, and ____ the book" (Daniel 12:4)
7. "When he hath ____ me, I shall come forth as gold" (Job 23:10)
8. "Is any thing too ____ for the Lord?" (Genesis 18:14)
9. Time past
10. Gives; pays
11. Go along with
13. "Laying up in ____ for themselves a good foundation against the time to come" (1 Timothy 6:19)
19. Loans
21. "O ____ me with thy salvation" (Psalm 106:4)
24. ____ and Remembrance (H. Wouk novel)
26. Up to the time of
28. "Woe unto you that laught now! for ye shall ____ and weep" (Luke 6:25)
29. KJV verb
30. "I go to ____ a place for you" (John 14:2)
31. Conger
33. Through (prefix)
34. Israeli statesman Levi
36. Aeries
38. More wan
40. Hirsute

41. Church leader
42. Bassoon, and others
44. "With what measure ye ____, it shall be measured to you" (Matthew 7:2)
45. The one who ____ blood shall bear his iniquity (Leviticus 17:14, 16)
48. Cartographer's triumph
50. ____ Novosti, Russian news agency
54. Not left (abbr.)

PUZZLE 22

ACROSS

1. "Behold the ____ of God, which taketh away the sin" (John 1:29)
5. "From the blood of ____ unto the blood of Zacharias" (Luke 11:51)
9. Afternoon repast
12. ____ code
13. Haircare name
14. Lacking polish
15. "Thou hast strengthened the ____ hands" (Job 4:3)
16. "The kingdom of heaven is like unto ____ hid in a field" (Matthew 13:44)
18. Parts of a tennis match
20. "I will ____ mine arrows upon them" (Deuteronomy 32:23)
21. Earthy
23. Greek letter
25. Broadcast
26. "And they came to the threshing-floor of ____" (Genesis 50:10)
28. "He ____ on the ground, and made clay" (John 9:6)
32. Party necessity
33. More pink
35. Avenue, in Avignon
36. Cozy place
38. Turner, for one
39. "The harvest is the ____ of the world" (Matthew 13:39)
40. This means business (abbr.)
42. ETS output (pl.)
44. One of the twelve cities of the tribe of Benjamin (Joshua 18:24)
47. "Let them sing aloud upon their ____" (Psalm 149:5)
48. "The Lord taketh ____ in his people" (Psalm 149:4)
51. Aden, for one
54. Poetic contraction
55. "They...were forbidden of the Holy Ghost to preach the word in ____" (Acts 16:6)
56. Great Lake
57. Arrest
58. "Our end is ____, our days are fulfilled" (Lamentations 4:18)
59. We should love in word, ____, and in truth (1 John 3)

DOWN

1. Before grace there was the ____
2. Linking verb
3. "Make ready quickly three ____ of fine meal" (Genesis 18:6)
4. Soaked up too much sun
5. "Many of them...which used curious ____ brought their books...and burned them" (Acts 19:19)
6. "Crossing the ____" (Tennyson work)
7. Christmas ____
8. "He that is ____ in the kingdom of heaven is greater than he" (Matthew 11:11)
9. Not fictional
10. Succeed the old-fashioned way
11. Speechless
17. De rigeur at resorts (pl.)
19. Thing to be shed
21. "Whosoever slayeth ____, vengeance shall be taken on him" (Genesis 4:15)
22. Texas university
23. Silents star Theda
24. Utopia
27. Chalky substance
29. Steady but unrelenting weight

30. "Thou shalt not approach to his wife: she is thine ____" (Leviticus 18:14)
31. Williams, and others
34. Assess
37. Feminine name
41. Hebrew month (Nehemiah 2:1)
43. "Out of his mouth went a sharp two____ sword" (Revelation 1:16)
44. U.S. ____ (sports event)
45. ____ bargain
46. "Your bones shall flourish like an ____" (Isaiah 66:14)

47. "I will meet them as a ____ that is bereaved" (Hosea 13:8)
49. "Teach the children of Judah the ____ of the bow" (2 Samuel 1:18)
50. Miss. Riv. arsenal
52. "He maketh me to ____ down in green pastures" (Psalm 23:2)
53. G-man

PUZZLE 23

ACROSS

1. Kitchen measure (abbr.)
4. "Let her ___: against the day of my burying hath she kept this" (John 12:7)
9. Baden-Baden is one
12. Titian's medium
14. "I have set before thee an ____ door" (Revelation 3:8)
15. Possesses
16. Evening wrap
18. "The ear trieth words, as the mouth ____ meat" (Job 34:3)
20. Strive for dominance
21. Rows
22. Hardly worth commenting on
26. "Leah said a troop cometh: and she called his name ____" (Genesis 30:11)
27. Actor Auberjonois
28. "They were swifter than eagles, they were stronger than ____" (2 Samuel 1:23)
30. Preposition
32. Univ. subj.
33. Collect collectibles
34. Verses to a Grecian urn
35. French conjunction
36. Diagram
37. Author unknown (abbr.)
38. Exclamation of achievement
39. "Thou ____ up the sum, full of wisdom" (Ezekiel 28:12)
41. Live like a longhorn
43. Leave out
44. Where ship is secured
46. Lake ____ (outdoor playground)
49. Hosp. facilities (pl.)
50. Affirm or attest to
52. Delhi "to go" garb
53. Born (Fr.)
54. African scavenger
55. Author Amy

DOWN

1. Basketball blunders (abbr.)
2. Portraitist's command
3. "He was ____ with twelve yoke of oxen" (1 Kings 19:19)
5. KJV exclamation
6. Elect
7. Spiffy
8. Certain sailors
9. Broken piece of pottery, KJV style
10. Touches lightly
11. Tree type
13. Demetrius, in *The Robe*
17. The family of ____, descendants of Gad (Numbers 26:16)
19. Prince of Wales, and others
22. "I give to eat of the ____ of life" (Revelation 2:7)
23. Torn apart
24. Feminine name
25. Ananias and Sapphira, to name two
29. Bones (comb. form)
30. Big deals
31. Abraham's abode
33. Son of Ahab (1 Kings 22:40)
34. "He that...meddleth with strife... is like ____ ____ [2 words] taketh a dog by the ears" (Proverbs 26:17)
36. Scorch
37. Witness Protection Program gift
38. Was no longer supine
40. Quantity (abbr.)
41. Former senator from Tennessee
42. Green monster
44. Door designation

45. Command to a horse
47. Mouth (pl.)
48. German article
51. TLC provider

PUZZLE 24

ACROSS

1. Kind of walker
4. One that sends hisses
7. What the diseased woman touched on Jesus' garment
10. "____ no man any thing, but to love one another" (Romans 13:8)
11. Capture, in a way
12. Son of Seth
14. Chicken, in Dodge City
16. Accomplished
17. Laughing syllable
19. ___head
20. "They ____ my path, they set forward my calamity" (Job 30:13)
21. Like 911
22. "The ____ enemy that shall be destroyed is death" (1 Corinthians 15:26)
24. Son of ___
25. Oil or water
26. King of Bashan (1 Kings 4:19)
27. "Arise, take up thy ____, and go unto thine house" (Matthew 9:6)
28. "Write in it with a man's ____" (Isaiah 8:1)
29. "I saw seven ____ candlesticks" (Revelation 1:12)
32. "Lord, they have killed thy prophets, and ____ down thine altars" (Romans 11:3)
35. Potato part
36. ____ potato
37. Bible language (abbr.)
38. "Jesus saith unto them, Come and ____" (John 21:12)
40. Funny person
41. "This is the whole ____ of man" (Ecclesiastes 12:13)

43. Masculine nickname
44. Knock
45. Sample
46. Revere(d) state (abbr.)
47. Douglas is one
48. Thing to be controlled
51. Average
53. ___-Gurion
54. Sprightly one
55. "He walketh through ____ places, seeking rest" (Luke 11:24)
56. Breadcrust, for example
57. Throw away

DOWN

1. "They rejoiced with exceeding great ____" (Matthew 2:10)
2. ____ struck
3. Painful cries
4. In a short time (arch.)
5. "A time to rend, and a time to ____" (Ecclesiastes 3:7)
6. Liquid measure (abbr.)
7. Son or daughter, most likely
8. "He that keepeth my works unto the ____, to him will I give power" (Revelation 2:26)
9. "Show Me" state (abbr.)
13. "Their tongue is as an arrow ____ out" (Jeremiah 9:8)
15. Put a match to
16. Tribe of Israel
18. Furniture wood
20. Consumed by, with "for"
21. Paul and Silas prayed and ____ in prison
22. Captain's journal
23. Times past
24. "Whom do ____ say that I am?" (Mark 8:27)

25. "Therefore shall he _____ in harvest, and have nothing" (Proverbs 20:4)
27. "The Lord shall hiss...for the _____ that is in the land of Assyria" (Isaiah 7:18)
28. Seed
30. Part of church calendar
31. Tie-_____
32. "A living _____ is better than a dead lion" (Ecclesiastes 9:4)
33. Mother's advice concerning broccoli
34. _____ run
36. Chance (arch.)

38. Item on an AKC document
39. Duke of Edom (Genesis 36:43)
40. Rage against
41. Far from brainy
42. "He shall show you a large _____ room furnished" (Luke 22:12)
44. Tim, for one
45. Post
47. _____ cry
48. Perfect score, sometimes
49. Father of Hophni (1 Samuel 1:3)
50. "Mayberry _____" (former TV show)
52. Publishing person (abbr.)
53. Live

ACROSS

1. Holiday symbol
4. "The ____ of the wicked shall be put out" (Proverbs 13:9)
8. Not as much
12. ____ reliever
13. Object of worship
14. Press
15. "____ far from me vanity and lies" (Proverbs 30:8)
17. Linking verb
19. KJV exclamation
20. Reverence
21. Pantry pest
22. What Nebuchadnezzar was washed with, in the wilderness
23. As thin as a ___
25. Fitting
26. "For my yoke is ____, and my burden is light" (Matthew 11:30)
27. Vase
28. Take in a little at a time, literally
29. Low island
30. State of the Southwest (abbr.)
31. "Thou ____ my wanderings: put thou my tears into thy bottle" (Psalm 56:8)
33. "Look!" to King James
35. Cow sound
36. Gershwin
37. "Man that is born of a woman is of ____ days and full of trouble" (Job 14:1)
38. Pump
40. Understand
41. "Then shall the ____ man leap as an hart" (Isaiah 35:6)
42. SRO show
43. Like a bassett hound's expression
44. ____ hen
45. Of Middle Eastern ancestry (abbr.)

46. "Make thee an ____ of gopher wood" (Genesis 6:14)
47. "Such ____ works are wrought by his hands" (Mark 6:2)
50. Very special
52. "Thou hast been in ____ the garden of God" (Ezekiel 28:13)
54. Kind of lamb in Nathan's symbolic story to David
55. Redact
56. "The Lord is my strength and ____" (Psalm 118:14)
57. Become soft

DOWN

1. "The Son of man is as a man taking a ____ journey" (Mark 13:34)
2. Put on ___
3. "That my joy might ____ in you" (John 15:11)
4. Animate
5. Summer drink
6. Detective's quest (abbr.)
7. Put down roots
8. Fabrication
9. Sound of hesitation
10. Shoe parts
11. Unsoiled; spotless
16. "I am like an ____ of the desert" (Psalm 102:6)
18. Not left (abbr.)
21. "I ____ mine heart to know...and to seek out wisdom" (Ecclesiastes 7:25)
22. "To proclaim...the ____ of vengeance of our God" (Isaiah 61:2)
23. "Ye did ____ well; who did hinder you" (Galatians 5:7)
24. Get equipped
25. Be in distress
26. Take a nibble

28. Baste
29. Jeff Davis's org.
31. Digit
32. Before
33. Haw's partner
34. Be in debt
35. "The ____ fell on Matthias; and he was numbered" (Acts 1:26)
37. God is our ___
38. "The Lord is thy ____ upon thy right hand" (Psalm 121:5)
39. "Paul dwelt two whole years in his own ____ house" (Acts 28:30)
40. "All things are for your ____" (2 Corinthians 4:15)

41. Journey jaunt
43. Dad might be one (abbr.)
44. Annex
46. "____ thou he that should come?" (Luke 7:19)
47. Fathers and uncles, for example
48. "____ of every sort shalt thou bring" (Genesis 6:19)
49. "Though he slay me, ____ will I trust in him" (Job 13:15)
51. "Gibeon...was greater than ____ and all the men...were mighty" (Joshua 10:2)
53. Act

PUZZLE 26

ACROSS

1. "Every one could sling stones at an hair breadth, and not____" (Judges 20:16)
5. "In their hands they shall ____ thee up lest...thou dash thy foot against a stone" (Matthew 4:6)
9. Before
12. Duke or duchess, for example
13. Word in a threat
14. Disagreement
15. Tribe of Israel
17. "So then they that are in the flesh cannot ____ God" (Romans 8:8)
19. This cookie didn't crumble (it's a success)
21. Lets up
22. Outgrowth
25. Linking verb
26. Canola, for one
27. "Joy that was set before him, endured the ____, despising the shame" (Hebrews 12:2)
29. Unit of weight (abbr.)
31. Behold's partner
32. "Behold an Israelite indeed, in whom is no ____" (John 1:47)
33. "They fled before the men of ____" (Joshua 7:4)
34. French conjunction
35. "This he said, not that he ____ for the poor" (John 12:6)
36. Consumed
37. With Aaron, he held up Moses' hands (Exodus 17)
38. "But ____ us from evil" (Matthew 6:13)
41. Maritime occurrence
43. "The third day he shall ____ again" (Matthew 20:19)
44. "Fallen ____ in Christ" (Christians who have already died) (1 Corinthians 15:18)
46. Stop on the journey from Egypt to Jordan (Numbers 33:27)
49. Tribe of Israel
50. "Hallowed be thy ____" (Matthew 6:9)
53. Continent
54. Hospital facility (abbr., pl.)
55. Sheet size
56. Ancient European

DOWN

1. Baby lamb's cry
2. April addressee
3. Take to ____ (or defeat handily, colloq.)
4. Pottery remains (arch.)
5. "How can these things ___?" (John 3:9)
6. It loops the Loop (abbr.)
7. Serpent
8. "Whom will ye that I ____ unto you, Barabbas or Jesus?" (Matthew 27:17)
9. Wipe away
10. "The desert shall...blossom as the ____" (Isaiah 35:1)
11. Part of the pasture populace (pl.)
16. Son of Peleg (Genesis 11:18)
18. Corn servings
20. Happen
22. "Make thee a fiery serpent and set it upon a ____" (Numbers 21:8)
23. Uproar
24. True's partner
28. Longer in the tooth
29. "It is vain for you to rise up early, to sit up ____" (Psalm 127:2)

30. Coffin and platform
32. Item of clothing
35. Find a solution
36. Disinclined
37. What are not barred (colloq.)
39. Illuminated
40. Ishmael's half-brother
41. Wise man
42. Peter, for one
45. "The Lord that delivered me out of the _____ of the lion" (1 Samuel 17:37)
47. To be under the weather
48. Panama, for one
51. Note on the diatonic scale

52. Printer's measure

PUZZLE 27

ACROSS

1. They give a hoot
5. Smite, modern style
9. Time of personal testing
10. "Every kind of beasts...hath been ____ of mankind" (James 3:7)
12. Rio ___
13. Officer of David who "was over the tribute" (2 Samuel 20:24)
15. Cereal grain
16. "He cannot ____ himself" (2 Timothy 2:13)
18. Trigonometric ratio
19. Healing plant
21. Put two and two together
23. Middle-school subj.
24. Egg size
26. One who grinds his teeth
28. "Stand in the ____ before me" (Ezekiel 22:30)
30. Cotton ___
31. God ____ those who honestly seek Him
35. Earl, for one
39. Ancient Scandinavian war horn
40. ____ de France
42. Dandelion, for one
43. To be (Fr.)
45. "I will...that men ____ every where, lifting up holy hands" (1 Timothy 2:8)
47. One beguiled by the serpent
48. Scoundrel (colloq.)
50. "Looking up to ____ he blessed them" (Luke 9:16)
52. Garden or grass, for example
53. Amend
54. What club coffers contain
55. Lunch orders (abbr.)

DOWN

1. "The Lord...doth take away from Jerusalem...the eloquent____" (Isaiah 3:1, 3)
2. "I count all things but loss...that I may ____ Christ" (Philippians 3:8)
3. Actor Alan
4. "Now I lay me down to ___"
5. ____ power
6. Young boy
7. Minor prophet
8. "____ the thought"
9. Singing syllables
11. "Praise him with the timbrel and ____" (Psalm 150:4)
12. Paul's was the high calling of God in Jesus Christ
14. Gutsy Golda
17. What husbands don't want wives to do
20. Served shirred, perhaps
22. "The Lord God had not caused it to ____ upon the earth" (Genesis 2:5)
25. Whence the wise men came
27. ____on-the-mountain
29. "Thou must prophesy again before many ____" (Revelation 10:11)
31. Played certain instruments
32. Old stringed instruments
33. Task to do
34. French preposition
36. "And levy a tribute unto the Lord...both of the persons, and of the ____" (Numbers 31:28)
37. Bar used to pry
38. "All the trees of ____, the choice and best of Lebanon" (Ezekiel 31:16)

41. "They...came into an harlot's house, named ____" (Joshua 2:1)
44. Firstborn of Isaac and Rebekah
46. Make oneself heard
49. Make ends meet, with "out"
51. Memo abbr.

PUZZLE 28

ACROSS

1. Polite word (pl.)
5. Seaport of Israel
9. Nocturnal creature
12. David or Solomon, perhaps
13. London's Abbey is one
14. Nineteenth-century American author
15. Prophetess and daughter of Phanuel
16. They respond to 911 (abbr.)
17. Like food or water
18. "Or if he shall ask an ____, will he offer him a scorpion?" (Luke 11:12)
20. Former P.M. of Israel
22. "____ not at all; neither by heaven" (Matthew 5:34)
24. Period
25. Simile syntax
27. One hundred fifty-one, to Livy
28. Hoover, for one
30. Large group
32. Trite phrase
34. Like one who "hath a devil" (John 10:20)
36. Always
37. "Be ye ____, and sin not" (Ephesians 4:26)
39. Regret
41. Before
42. Movie rating (abbr.)
43. Texas Tech's ____ Raiders
45. Like a foyer
47. Room's partner
49. Just a ___
50. Asaph the ____ (2 Chronicles 29:30)
52. Have a bite
54. After the crucifixion, the soldiers gambled for Jesus' ___

57. Hole-making tool
58. "His clothes shall be rent and his head ____" (Leviticus 13:45)
59. Prophet who follows Joel
60. Still
61. Former British P.M. Anthony
62. It comes with the territory, in the kitchen

DOWN

1. Retreat, perhaps
2. Electrically charged atom
3. "Be ye transformed by the ____ of your mind" (Romans 12:2)
4. ___struck
5. Linking verb
6. Search thoroughly
7. Demolished (as in Psalm 137:7)
8. Sullivan, for one
9. Pull to ____
10. "One ____ is past and behold there come two" (Revelation 9:12)
11. "He was ____ as a sheep to the slaughter" (Acts 8:32)
17. "As vinegar upon ____, so is he that singeth songs to an heavy heart" (Proverbs 25:20)
19. Tribe of Israel
21. "There is but one ____" (1 Corinthians 8:6)
22. "His ____ was in his hand: and he drew near the Philistine" (1 Samuel 17:40)
23. Slam against
25. _____ Fisher Hall, in NYC
26. Withered
27. "O ____ your hands, all ye people" (Psalm 47:1)
29. Deface

Crossword grid with numbered cells:

Row 1: 1, 2, 3, 4, ■, 5, 6, 7, 8, ■, 9, 10, 11
Row 2: 12, 13, ■, 14
Row 3: 15, 16, ■, 17
Row 4: ■, 18, 19, 20, 21
Row 5: 22, 23, 24, 25, 26
Row 6: 27, 28, 29, 30, 31
Row 7: 32, 33, 34, 35, 36
Row 8: 37, 38, 39, 40, 41
Row 9: 42, 43, 44, 45, 46
Row 10: 47, 48, 49
Row 11: 50, 51, 52, 53, 54, 55, 56
Row 12: 57, 58, 59
Row 13: 60, 61, 62

31. "But be of good cheer; I have _____ the world" (John 16:33)
33. "He is risen from the dead: so the last _____ shall be worse than the first" (Matthew 27:64)
35. Date _____ (library logo)
38. KJV affirmative
40. Naval officer (abbr.)
44. "Fear and _____ shall fall upon them" (Exodus 15:16)
46. Father of Abram
47. Update of biblical girdle

48. "For I will not _____ to speak of any of those things which Christ hath not wrought" (Romans 15:18)
50. " _____ what?"
51. Lea dowager
53. "Praise the Lord with...an instrument of _____ strings" (Psalm 33:2)
55. Flamboyant wrap
56. NYC time
58. Exist

PUZZLE 29

ACROSS

1. Iowa city
5. Apple variety
9. Thirty Years' ___
12. "I will bring again the captivity of ___" (Jeremiah 49:39)
13. Levitical city of refuge (1 Chronicles 6:73)
14. Samuel's mentor
15. Continent (abbr.)
16. Wired, with "on"
18. "They shall ___ the whirlwind: it hath no stalk" (Hosea 8:7)
19. "My Father giveth you the ___ bread from heaven" (John 6:32)
20. Where the prodigal son dined out
22. Live; realize one's potential
23. "The ___ of wisdom is above rubies" (Job 28:18)
25. "If the good man...had known what hour the ___ would come" (Luke 12:39)
27. Deceased
28. Facade
29. Kind of number
32. Ember residue
33. Trunk "tenant"
34. KJV deer
35. Born (Fr.)
36. Pitchfork hazard
37. Winter plague
38. Adhere
40. Fish or fight
41. Hush!
43. Linking verb
44. "I was an hungred and ye gave me no ___" (Matthew 25:42)
45. ___ and Gown
47. Unplanned information channel (colloq.)

48. Son of Judah (Genesis 38)
50. Used to row the boat
51. Opera solo
53. "At ___" (heard at certain camps)
55. Meddle
56. Be introduced
57. "I am instructed...both to abound and to suffer ___" (Philippians 4:12)

DOWN

1. Number of lepers in Samaria who were healed by Jesus (Luke 17)
2. In the manner of
3. One of the Kettles
4. "And they shall ___ him in an hundred shekels of silver" (Deuteronomy 22:19)
5. "The chariots shall ___ in the streets" (Nahum 2:4)
6. Number of lepers in Samaria who praised God (Luke 17)
7. Bar Harbor state (abbr.)
8. Auntie ___ (L. F. Baum character)
9. Tiny and young
10. Southern state (abbr.)
11. Ready
17. "Let us not be weary...for in ___ season we shall reap" (Galatians 6:9)
18. Deli staple
19. "Bring ye all the ___ into the storehouse" (Malachi 3:10)
20. Lion's portion
21. Horologist's concern, in a way
23. ___ of action
24. Level, as a building (Brit.)

25. "First, I _____ my God through Jesus Christ for you all" (Romans 1:8)
26. Didn't remember
28. _____ Islands
30. Dreary
31. "Let us not love in word...but in _____" (1 John 3:18)
33. Agitate
37. Become aware of
39. Ecru
40. The Great ___
41. Organ option
42. "As small as the _____ frost on the ground" (Exodus 16:14)

44. "I have _____ to eat that ye know not of" (John 4:32)
46. Droll
47. _____ low
48. Compass dir.
49. Buttons
51. Exist
52. In ___
54. One (Scot.)

PUZZLE 30

ACROSS

1. "God clave an hollow place that was in the ____, and there came water thereout" (Judges 15:19)
4. Prepare fruit
8. Whatever ____ you
12. Jurist Fortas
13. Black
14. Dagger
15. "He ____ my strength in the way" (Psalm 102:23)
17. Permanent mark
18. Evidence of beating
19. Sesame, for one
20. Northwest ____ (abbr.)
21. "Shoot out thine ____, and destroy them" (Psalm 144:6)
24. Ate out
27. Linking verb
28. Comprehend
29. Son of Zeus
30. "How can a man be born when he is ___?" (John 3:4)
31. *Dead* ____ (Dick Francis classic)
32. French pronoun
33. Hole-making tool
34. Amusement park amusements
35. Begin a conversation
37. Wager
38. Hurry (arch.)
39. Punish (arch.)
43. Steakhouse selection, perhaps
45. "Though they would have cast anchors out of the ____" (Acts 27:30)
47. Cary Grant, once
48. Father of Azariah (2 Chronicles 15:1)
49. Paris summer
50. Challenge
51. Whirlpool
52. Affirmative vote

DOWN

1. Spielberg film
2. Aid's partner
3. ____ thin
4. "There was none that moved the wing or opened the mouth, or ____" (Isaiah 10:14)
5. Son of Ner (2 Samuel 2:8)
6. "Asahel was as light of foot as a wild ____" (2 Samuel 2:18)
7. Like omega
8. Son of Kohath (1 Chronicles 6:22)
9. "And they wrought onyx stones ____ in ouches of gold" (Exodus 39:6)
10. Bucolic locale
11. Indian weight
16. Unclean birds (Deuteronomy 14:13)
19. Pay dirt
21. Son of Bela (Numbers 26:40)
22. Used to be
23. Cupboard collections, as in dishes
24. Fruit of the palm
25. Smooth
26. One close by
27. Cheer competitor
30. "____ no man any thing, but to love" (Romans 13:8)
31. Refers to
33. Mature
34. "The wrath of the Lord arose against his people, till there was no ____" (2 Chronicles 36:16)
36. Seat location
37. Told all
40. Feminine name

41. Bethlehem: _____ of David
42. Fencing gear
43. Exterminate
44. Lupino
45. Nemesis
46. "The _____ number...is to be redeemed" (Numbers 3:48)

PUZZLE 31

ACROSS

1. This admits attorneys
4. Tribe of Israel
9. Son of King Abijam
12. KJV verb
13. "The last ____ of that man is worse than the first" (Luke 11:26)
14. Atlantic state (abbr.)
15. Exist
16. "Abstain from ____ lusts which war against the soul" (1 Peter 2:11)
18. Apiece (abbr.)
19. Golf goal
21. Golf bag contents
23. "I will not give sleep to mine ____" (Psalm 132:4)
25. Aerie
26. Prophetic O.T. book (abbr.)
28. Entreat
30. What may be let out
33. Linking verb
34. "____ yourselves likewise with the same mind" (1 Peter 4:1)
35. "As it was in the days of ____, so shall it be" (Luke 17:26)
36. Del ____, CA
37. Fades
39. "There was no room for them in the ____" (Luke 2:7)
40. In short order (arch.)
42. ____ man (jazz player)
44. King of the Moabites (Numbers 22:4)
46. Dinner table favorites, especially with children
49. Linking verb
50. Populates
54. Twelve Step gp.
55. Under-____ (beach hazard)
57. Hebrew month
58. ATM number
59. "It will be fair weather: for the ____ is red" (Matthew 16:2)
60. Undergarments
61. What Hophni and Phineas took into battle

DOWN

1. Bunyon's ox
2. ____ code
3. Correct (abbr.)
4. "Where is the promise of his coming? for since the fathers fell ____" (2 Peter 3:4)
5. Sault ____ Marie
6. Possesses
7. Ordinal suffix
8. Depended on
9. Classified info
10. "God hath ____ mine affliction" (Genesis 31:42)
11. Exclamation of dismay
16. Summer pest
17. Time period (abbr., pl.)
20. "To the ____ assembly and church of the firstborn" (Hebrews 12:23)
22. First judge of Israel
24. "In the midst of the elders, stood a Lamb as it had been ____" (Revelation 5:6)
25. "Your ____ are written in heaven" (Luke 10:20)
26. Flood preventer, sometimes
27. Former NFL coach Parseghian
29. "Ye do ____, not knowing the scriptures" (Matthew 22:29)
31. Many moons

32. "Let no man glory in ___. For all things are yours" (1 Corinthians 3:21)
37. "Who sent ____ and wonders into the midst of thee, O Egypt" (Psalm 135:9)
38. Mythological nymphs
41. Part of fabric
43. PC operating system
44. Cavern dwellers
45. Lose control, with "run"
47. Hideaway
48. Went down
51. What was poured on Saul's head
52. Greek letter
53. Sitting down, you get this
56. Western state (abbr.)
58. State College state (abbr.)

PUZZLE 32

ACROSS

1. White, for one
5. "For I have no man...who will naturally ____ for your state" (Philippians 2:20)
9. Kind of truck
12. Minor prophet
13. So be it
14. Female lea dweller
15. 3.1416
16. Sixties-style dress
18. "They compassed me about like ____" (Psalm 118:12)
19. "She shall shave her head and ____ her nails" (Deuteronomy 21:12)
20. Greek letter
22. NY or CA
23. Greek isle
25. "Do ye think that the scripture ____ in vain" (James 4:5)
27. Definitely pink
28. Nick Charles, aka The ____ Man
29. Exclamation of discovery
32. ____ on parle francais
33. "For if ye love them which love you, what ____ have ye?" (Luke 6:32)
34. ____ fried
35. Barbara ____ Geddes
36. Baby and bath, to name two
37. "And he ____ and touched his tongue" (Mark 7:33)
38. "Is the Lord's hand waxed ___?" (Numbers 11:23)
40. Prophets
41. Athens is here (abbr.)
43. "Joseph...was the son of his ____ age" (Genesis 37:3)
44. ____ there, done that

45. "The workman is worthy of his ____" (Matthew 10:10)
47. Come together; touch
48. "Arise, go up to ____" (Joshua 8:1)
50. Mess up
51. Shut's partner
53. Apparent one
55. Asiatic deer
56. Accustomed
57. "I'm all ___"

DOWN

1. "The trees of the Lord are full of ____" (Psalm 104:16)
2. French friend
3. Biblical exclamation
4. "He hath regarded the low ____ of his handmaiden" (Luke 1:48)
5. Hawaiian product, for short
6. Quantity (abbr.)
7. Concerning
8. ___-gedi (where David dwelt for a time)
9. To a ___
10. Is beholden to
11. Author Nathanael
17. Before
18. Bridle part
19. Pauline's adventures of filmdom
20. "Whom God hath raised up, having loosed the ____ of death" (Acts 2:24)
21. Kind of hole
23. "Where no oxen are, the ____ is clean" (Proverbs 14:4)
24. 3 K or 5 K, for example
25. "Thou ____ love thy neighbor" (Romans 13:9)

26. "He...began to tell them what things should _____ unto him" (Mark 10:32)
28. "The Lord called Samuel again the _____ time" (1 Samuel 3:8)
30. Absalom's stunning feature
31. "The _____ are a people not strong" (Proverbs 30:25)
33. Hand or power
37. Rage inside
39. Salsa choice
40. Jurisdiction of a bishop
41. Ancient Hebrew dry measure
42. Deli order

44. "He hath _____ his bow, and made it ready" (Psalm 7:12)
46. Linking verb
47. "I will...that _____ pray everywhere" (1 Timothy 2:8)
48. Broadcast
49. Government agency (abbr.)
51. Ouch!
52. River in Italy
54. Per person (abbr.)

ACROSS

1. "Until the day dawn, and the day
   ____ arise" (2 Peter 1:19)
5. "Believe not every spirit, but
   ____ the spirits" (1 John 4:1)
8. Some circles
12. "Take thine ____, eat, drink, and
    be merry" (Luke 12:19)
13. Do garden work
14. Wild rest stop
15. Operatic highlight
16. *Mange*, in Marshalltown
17. Land measure
18. "Let them be for signs, and for
    ____, and for day, and years"
    (Genesis 1:14)
20. Pine
21. Exclamation of pain
22. Item to do
24. Newsman Phillips
27. Laughing sound
28. Moisture
31. Holds the deed to
32. "We have also a more ____ word
    of prophecy" (2 Peter 1:19)
33. Forest female
34. "If God ____ for us, who can be
    against us?" (Romans 8:31)
36. "We pray you in Christ's ____,
    be ye reconciled to God"
    (2 Corinthians 5:20)
37. "They wandered in deserts, and
    in mountains, and in ____"
    (Hebrews 11:38)
39. ____ of the Chaldees
40. Late actor Ames
42. Survived in water
47. Kind of scale
48. "Ye ____ bought with a price"
    (1 Corinthians 6:20)
49. Tabu, to toddler

50. Greek letter (pl.)
51. Nothing
52. Oaf; bully
53. Black, for one
54. Kind of glass
55. Sea bird

DOWN

1. "The gathering together of the
   waters called he ____"
   (Genesis 1:10)
2. "The devil threw him down and
   ____ him" (Luke 9:42)
3. "The churches of ____ salute
   you" (1 Corinthians 16:19)
4. "Produce your cause...bring forth
   your strong ____, saith the King
   of Jacob" (Isaiah 41:21)
5. There's partner
6. Sunday entree
7. "____ not I, but Christ liveth in
   me" (Galatians 2:20)
8. "The Lord is not ____ concerning his promise" (2 Peter 3:9)
9. Every
10. Soggy ground
11. Anger
19. "____ no man any thing, but to
    love" (Romans 13:8)
20. King of Judah; son of Abijam
23. Exclamation of delight
24. Earth
25. When this many are gathered
    together, the Lord is present
26. Christians worship the ____ true
    God
28. "A word spoken in ____ season,
    how good is it"
    (Proverbs 15:23)
29. Historical period
30. Unite

Crossword Grid

1	2	3	4	■	5	6	7	■	8	9	10	11
12				■	13			■	14			
15				■	16			■	17			
18			19			■	20					■
■	■	■	21		■	22	23			■	■	■
24	25	26			■	27			■	28	29	30
31				■	■	■	■	■	32			
33			■	34	35		■	36				
■	■	37			■	38		39			■	■
■	40	41			■	42	43			44	45	46
47				■	48			■	49			
50				■	51			■	52			
53				■	54			■	55			

32. "How shall we sing the Lord's song in a _____ land?" (Psalm 137:4)
34. ___-oni, Rachel's youngest
35. Printer's measure
36. "A Boy Named _____" (J. Cash hit)
37. KJV verb
38. Airport runway
40. Recently, with "of"
41. Showing no favoritism (Fr.)
43. Call on for help
44. "Behold, I stand at the _____" (Revelation 3:20)
45. _____ Church, Virginia (site of 1864 battle)
46. Well _____
47. *Charlotte's* _____ (E.B. White classic)
48. Reply (abbr.)

PUZZLE 34

ACROSS

1. "Call me not Naomi, call me ____" (Ruth 1:20)
5. Bunch of bubbles
9. Paramedic's report (abbr.)
12. "The slaughter of Midian at the rock of ____" (Isaiah 10:26)
13. "Every ____ word that men shall speak, they shall give account" (Matthew 12:36)
14. There's the ___
15. "She...began to ____ his feet with tears" (Luke 7:38)
16. Burden
17. Compass dir.
18. "Let us build us a city and ____, whose top may reach unto heaven" (Genesis 11:4)
20. Lets off fumes
22. Ship to ___
24. Team _____, Olympics competitor
25. Attitude
26. Has ___
29. "It shall be even given thee to the ____ of the kingdom" (Esther 5:3)
33. Creative concept
35. "I will send a ____ , saying, Go, find the arrows" (1 Samuel 20:21)
36. Golden calf, for one
37. More is ___
38. Telegram word
40. United
41. Ram's mate
43. Captured, in a way
45. Lion's portion
48. "What is the chaff to the ___?" (Jeremiah 23:28)
50. Require effort
51. "He himself stayed in ____ for a season" (Acts 19:22)
53. Become bored
56. Linking verb
57. ____ stop
58. "Whatsoever shall be given you in that ____, that speak ye" (Mark 13:11)
59. Affirmative
60. Overeat, almost
61. Dagger

DOWN

1. Weekend job, for many
2. Son of Jether (1 Chronicles 7:38)
3. Gives new life, as the Lord
4. "Him shall the people curse, nations shall ____ him" (Proverbs 24:24)
5. Rank's partner
6. Scent
7. In the manner of
8. "Thy kingdom is divided, and given to the ____ and the Persians" (Daniel 5:28)
9. Three (Ger.)
10. Fire
11. Fortas and others
19. Where one surfs
21. Mother, hello (abbr.)
22. "Strengthen their mast, they could not spread the ____" (Isaiah 33:23)
23. "____ us from the face of him that sitteth on the throne" (Revelation 6:16)
24. Cancel; annul
27. In addition

28. Partake
30. "Ye have received the Spirit of ____, whereby we cry, Abba, Father" (Romans 8:15)
31. Single
32. "Then all the disciples forsook him, and ____" (Matthew 26:56)
34. Tribe of Israel (var.)
39. ____millennialism
42. Becomes useless, with "out"
44. Vows
45. "None can ____ his hand" (Daniel 4:35)
46. Unclean animal (Leviticus 11:6)
47. Cutting tools

48. Knew; learned (arch.)
49. "____ the evil" (Amos 5:15)
52. Aegean, for one
54. Regret
55. Poetic contraction

ACROSS

1. Woolly ones
5. Under the weather
8. Mull over
12. Imply
13. Feminine Israeli name
14. Covenant
15. Make null
16. Attila, for one
17. Zone
18. "As newborn babes, _____ the sincere milk of the word" (1 Peter 2:2)
20. "_____ is all, and in all" (Colossians 3:11)
22. Cable, for one
23. Hairpin curve
24. "In thy fear will I _____ toward thy holy temple" (Psalm 5:7)
28. Temporary dwellings
32. "For Adam was first formed, then _____" (1 Timothy 2:13)
33. Gratuity
35. Vowel trio
36. "To be a reproach and a proverb, a _____ and a curse" (Jeremiah 24:9)
39. "The dragon shalt thou _____ under feet" (Psalm 91:13)
42. _____ drum
44. "Ye _____ of your father the devil" (John 8:44)
45. Graven image, perhaps
48. Mental pictures
52. Hope
53. Donkey
55. Disreputable establishment
56. Sheltered side
57. "A faithful witness will not _____" (Proverbs 14:5)
58. Appliance

59. "The day of the Lord is _____" (Joel 3:14)
60. Sra, in Sarasota
61. Left

DOWN

1. Son of Gera, the second judge of Israel (Judges 3:15)
2. "Woe to them that are mighty to drink _____" (Isaiah 5:22)
3. "The Creator of the _____ of the earth, fainteth not" (Isaiah 40:28)
4. Group of philosophers who met Paul at Athens (Acts 17:18)
5. "They that do such things shall not _____ the kingdom of God" (Galatians 5:21)
6. President Hoover's wife, familiarly
7. Masculine name
8. Rough; earthy
9. Mata _____
10. Summers, in Nice
11. Reporter's question
19. Stadium sound
21. Honolulu's time zone
24. _____ paint
25. Eggs
26. Father of Serug (Genesis 11:20)
27. "To him was given the key of the bottomless _____" (Revelation 9:1)
29. Snooze
30. Up to that point (var.)
31. Feminine nickname
34. The children of the Proverbs 31 woman call her blessed, and the husband _____ her
37. "They are all delivered unto death, to the _____ parts of the earth" (Ezekiel 31:14)

38. Greek letter
40. "The isles shall wait upon me, and on mine ____ shall they trust" (Isaiah 51:5)
41. Bucolic spot
43. King's bailiwick
45. ____ song
46. Mosaic piece
47. On a steamer
49. "____ unto the Lord the glory due unto his name" (Psalm 96:8)
50. Tied
51. Dispatched
54. Title of respect

PUZZLE 36

ACROSS

1. Cleo's killer
4. Asa or Ahab
8. Perfect
12. "They cast ____, that is, the lot, before Haman" (Esther 3:7)
13. One who sold his birthright
14. "As he saith also in ____, I will call them my people" (Romans 9:25)
15. Where one uses a wood
16. "Six ____ shalt thou labour and do all thy work" (Exodus 20:9)
17. Reporter's question
18. "There shall come a ____ out of Jacob and a Sceptre shall rise" (Numbers 24:17)
20. Word's partner
21. "Stretch out the ____ that is in thy hand toward Ai" (Joshua 8:18)
23. Greek letter
25. To exhibit exhaustion
26. Burdened one
27. Golden State (abbr.)
29. Godfrey, to friends
30. "The word is nigh thee, even in thy mouth, and in thy ____" (Romans 10:8)
31. "For the Father...hath committed all judgment unto the ____" (John 5:22)
32. Bible div.
33. "Ye shall be baptized with the Holy Ghost not many days ____" (Acts 1:5)
34. KJV verb
35. Out of (arch.)
36. Says "whoa"
37. "I am the ____ vine" (John 15:1)
38. "Nadab and Abihu...offered strange ____ before the Lord" (Leviticus 10:1)
39. Hurries
40. Speed
42. Compass dir.
45. Opposed to aweather
46. "In ____ there was a voice heard, lamentation" (Matthew 2:18)
47. Iowa college
48. Kind of hall
49. Memo part
50. Before

DOWN

1. "A bishop the must be...____ to teach" (1 Timothy 3:2)
2. Betty White role on "Mary Tyler Moore" TV show
3. "God is...a very ____ help in trouble" (Psalm 46:1)
4. "Arabia, and all the princes of ____...in these were thy merchants" (Ezekiel 27:21)
5. Danube tributary
6. Negative vote
7. Masculine nickname
8. American social reformer Julia
9. Son of Nun of the tribe of Ephraim (Numbers 13:8)
10. "I am instructed...both to abound and to suffer ____" (Philippians 4:12)
11. Poetic contraction
19. Make lace
20. KJV verb
21. Measure of length
22. Say adieu
23. "____ hither thy finger, and behold my hands" (John 20:27)

24. Tortoise's opponent
26. "My people are ____ to back sliding from me" (Hosea 11:7)
27. Pasture youngster
28. They head for the hills
30. Now's partner
31. "Let the lying lips be put to ____" (Psalm 31:18)
33. Provides shelter
34. "We do not ____ after the flesh" (2 Corinthians 10:3)
35. Loosens
36. "So ____ gave Solomon cedar trees and fir trees" (1 Kings 5:10)

37. Game piece
38. "His ____ went throughout all Syria" (Matthew 4:24)
39. Son of Noah
40. Every third (comb. form)
41. "____ thou not the bread of him that hath an evil eye" (Proverbs 23:6)
43. Conjunction
44. Shoe width

PUZZLE 37

ACROSS

1. Atlas and Apennines (abbr.)
4. "Is there no ____ in Gilead?" (Jeremiah 8:22)
8. Son of Omri; notoriously evil king
12. Gershwin
13. Great Lake
14. KJV verb
15. Complete collections
17. "Thou shalt not plow with an ox and an ____ together" (Deuteronomy 22:10)
18. Curtain or horse
19. Canines, for example
21. Stage direction
23. Legal object
25. Chemical suffix
26. Certain physician (abbr.)
28. "The yoke shall be destroyed because of the ____" (Isaiah 10:27)
32. ____ ear
33. "Whatsoever a man soweth, that shall he also ____" (Galatians 6:7)
34. Energy unit
35. Mad at
36. "They ____ my path, they set forward my calamity" (Job 30:13)
37. "There were set there six ____ of stone" (John 2:6)
39. Elder (abbr.)
40. "The everlasting ____, the Lord" (Isaiah 40:28)
41. One fleet of foot in the forest
42. Grand ____ auto
44. "Let them praise his name in the ____" (Psalm 149:3)
48. "____ went before the ark" (2 Samuel 6:4)
50. Linking verb
52. "____ my lips"
53. Works like a gem
54. Steadfast
56. KJV grain
57. Aid's partner
58. Saline drop
59. "When we came to the ____, that we opened our sacks" (Genesis 43:21)

DOWN

1. "There went up a ____ from the earth and watered" (Genesis 2:6)
2. Birch or ginkgo
3. Make contented
4. "____ it ever so humble..."
5. Son of Jether (1 Chronicles 7:38)
6. Feminine name
7. "A thorn in the flesh, the ____ of Satan" (2 Corinthians 12:7)
8. "____ in me, and I in you" (John 15:4)
9. Animal not to be eaten (Deuteronomy 14:7)
10. Hubbub
11. Actor Cross
16. Sunset, for one
20. Coop dowager
22. Participle suffix
24. Hardly fickle
26. Gossip, literally (colloq.)
27. Addition column
28. "God is thy refuge, and underneath are the everlasting ____" (Deuteronomy 33:27)
29. "Thou art ____, O Lord" (Psalm 119:151)
30. Paddle
31. NYC subway

32. "Is any thing ___ hard for the Lord?" (Genesis 18:14)
35. Asparagus unit
37. Sorrow
38. "The staff of his shoulder, the ___ of his oppressor" (Isaiah 9:4)
40. "The Holy ___ shall come upon thee" (Luke 1:35)
42. ___ and again
43. Colorfast
45. Father of Salathiel (Luke 3:27)
46. "Whosoever slayeth ___, vengeance shall be taken on him" (Genesis 4:15)

47. Idyllic spot
48. Exclamation
49. Where the action is
51. Baseball stat.
55. Son of Judah (1 Chronicles 2:3)

ACROSS

1. Sign of the end times (Matthew 24:6)
5. "Fear God and ____ his commandments" (Ecclesiastes 12:13)
9. Trucker's "motel"
12. "He [Isaac] called the name of the well ____" (Genesis 26:20)
13. Exclamation
14. Tint
15. Sinks
17. "I was afraid, and went and hid thy ____" (Matthew 25:25)
19. ____ and the Thummin (Exodus 28:30)
20. "My servant ____ at home sick" (Matthew 8:6)
21. Puts an end to
23. Parts of capitols
25. Charade
26. In the near future (arch.)
28. "Buy the truth and ____ it not" (Proverbs 23:23)
31. Preposition
32. Church part (pl.)
34. That is (abbr.)
35. "Ye may rejoice, and that I may be the ____ sorrowful" (Philippians 2:28)
38. Nuisance
39. Promise Keepers attendees
40. "Ye shall receive ____, after that the Holy Ghost is come" (Acts 1:8)
42. "____ your ways and your doings" (Jeremiah 7:3)
44. "There ____ from heaven a great light" (Acts 22:6)
46. Actor Thicke
47. Unleashed

49. "Those who by reason of use have their ____ exercised to discern" (Hebrews 5:14)
52. Holiday, for one
53. Choose's cohort
55. Settle in a cozy spot
56. French pronoun
57. "Thou hadst cast me...in the midst of the ____" (Jonah 2:3)
58. "The poison of ____ is under their lips" (Romans 3:13)

DOWN

1. Entanglement
2. Good king of Judah
3. Consequence
4. Avoid
5. Abyssinian weight
6. Chicago transport (abbr.)
7. "In the day you ____ thereof, then your eyes shall be opened" (Genesis 3:5)
8. "Sing unto the Lord with...the voice of a ____" (Psalm 98:5)
9. "Hast thou not...curdled me like ____" (Job 10:10)
10. Orpah, to Obed
11. House, in Hebrew
16. Hebrew month
18. "Behold, thou [Samson] hast mocked me [Delilah], and told me ____" (Judges 16:10)
21. Greet
22. Teen trauma
23. Capital of Delaware
24. Singles
27. Back of the neck
29. Property claim
30. Let borrow
33. Not fresh

36. Forks' cohorts
37. "As my beloved _____ I warn you" (1 Corinthians 4:14)
39. Monthly occurrence
41. Mourns
43. "Our fathers did eat _____ in the desert" (John 6:31)
44. Skirt feature
45. Practice and practice and practice
46. Queries
48. "To live is Christ and to _____ is gain" (Philippians 1:21)
50. Extra sense (abbr.)

51. Byways (abbr.)
54. About (abbr.)

PUZZLE 39

ACROSS

1. Buys (tickets) for later profit
7. "Believe on the Lord Jesus Christ, and thou shalt be ____" (Acts 16:31)
12. "An inheritance may be gotten ____ at the beginning" (Proverbs 20:21)
14. John, on Patmos
15. Luc, to Lisette
16. Kind of shot or shirt
17. Napa Valley sight (pl.)
18. Depilatory brand
20. "The ____ of sin is death" (Romans 6:23)
22. Note on the diatonic scale
23. Mete out
25. Bleed, as madras
26. Body of water (Fr.)
27. "Lo, I see four men ____, walking in the midst of the fire" (Daniel 3:25)
29. Horse hair
30. Aircraft authority
32. "Remember how ____ my time is" (Psalm 89:47)
34. 1/1000 of an inch (pl.)
35. Has strong feelings about
37. Ocean (abbr.)
38. Solidify
39. "Who hath...____ out heaven with the span" (Isaiah 40:12)
43. Borders VA and MD
44. Sewing fundamentals
46. "____ thyself, and come down from the cross" (Mark 15:30)
47. Interjection
48. Conjunction
49. Shoe size
51. Sue ____, honey brand
52. Traversed by *les bateaux mouches*
54. RSVP request
56. Ash and aspen
57. Wears; dons

DOWN

1. Columnist Alexander
2. "It is easier for a ____ to go through the eye of a needle" (Matthew 19:24)
3. Father of Seraiah (1 Chronicles 4:35)
4. Army officer (abbr.)
5. Pothole's cousin
6. Whole bunch
7. "I will serve thee ____ years for Rachel" (Genesis 29:18)
8. Alignment between countries
9. French export, to the French
10. Earth or air, for example
11. "Master...do for us whatsoever we shall ____" (Mark 10:35)
13. "Receive my sayings; and the ____ of thy life shall be many" (Proverbs 4:10)
19. Road trip expenses, sometimes
21. "That he was gone to be ____ with a man that is a sinner" (Luke 19:7)
24. As well
26. "Neither shalt thou ____ the corners of thy beard" (Leviticus 19:27)
28. Further; additional
29. Husband of Zipporah
30. He doesn't want to be called for a balk
31. "Love worketh no ____ to his neighbour" (Romans 13:10)
33. Haw's partner
34. "Thou ____ him a little lower than the angels" (Hebrews 2:7)

36. Change
38. Stations (Fr.)
40. Bible mount near Nazareth
41. Occurrence
42. "Ye have put off the old man
    with his ____" (Colossians 3:9)
44. Exhausted, with "in"
45. Understands
50. Particularly (abbr.)
53. Common abbr.
55. River in Italy

PUZZLE 40

ACROSS

1. Revolutionary hero Nathan
5. Step made by faith
9. Age of Methuselah when he had a son: one hundred eighty-____ (Genesis 5:25)
10. Aerie dweller
12. This may include "or else"
13. Most faithful
15. "There stood before the river a ____ which had two horns" (Daniel 8:3)
16. Treasured, in a way
18. Assess
19. Herdsman of Tekoia whom God called to be a prophet
21. Rod and ____
23. Bishopric
24. Noted Quaker family, and others
26. Chooses
28. At odds (abbr.)
30. Songdom's "gal"
31. "The way of man is ____ and strange" (Proverbs 21:8)
35. Is diminished
39. "Go, sell the ____, and pay thy debt" (2 Kings 4:7)
40. He went searching for his father's lost donkeys
42. Neap, for one
43. "Incline not my heart to any ____ thing" (Psalm 141:4)
45. Sesquicentennial segment
47. Mature
48. Stern
50. Like-____ (kindred spirit)
52. "The angels shall...____ the wicked from among the just" (Matthew 13:49)
53. Ezekiel saw a valley that was full of ____
54. Takes no action
55. "There shall come forth a rod out of the ____ of Jesse" (Isaiah 11:1)

DOWN

1. Mount on the northeastern boundary of Palestine (Joshua 12:1)
2. Roadway (abbr.)
3. Seep
4. Door direction
5. Colossians and Philippians, familiarly
6. What one lends
7. "The words of ___the son of Jakeh, even the prophecy" (Proverbs 30:1)
8. "Do I seek to ____ men?" (Galatians 1:10)
9. "Let them be confounded and put to ____" (Psalm 35:4)
11. Fragrant compound
12. Sand, for one
14. Wooden pegs
17. Vitality
20. Twentieth-century English novelist
22. "His ____ also shall not wither" (Psalm 1:3)
25. LaCosta, and others
27. Apartment
29. "He had offered up ____ and supplications with strong crying" (Hebrews 5:7)
31. Those opposed
32. Splits
33. Mount of ___
34. ____ date
36. "Thou shalt also be...a royal ____ in the hand of thy God" (Isaiah 62:3)

37. "These things, saith hc which hath the sharp sword with two ____" (Revelation 2:12)
38. ____ money
41. "Two ____ of the first year for a sacrifice of peace" (Leviticus 23:19)
44. Israel's high priest had to descend from this tribe
46. Lose control
49. Soak flax
51. Compass dir.

PUZZLE 41

ACROSS

1. Cartographer's creation
4. Had a stroke
8. Captain Hook's henchman
12. Mother of Hezekiah (2 Kings 18:2)
13. "The king arose, and ____ his garments" (2 Samuel 13:31)
14. "I ____ you!"
15. "My money is ___; and lo, it is even in my sack" (Genesis 42:28)
17 Deserve
18. Mar, in a way
19. "Beware of the scribes, which love...the chief ____ in the synagogues" (Mark 12:38,39)
21. English breakfast, for one
23. Keeps away from
26. Cathedral feature
29. "The vine languisheth, all the merry hearted do ____" (Isaiah 24:7)
32. Norma ____ (Sally Field role)
33. "He that hath clean hands and a ____ heart" (Psalm 24:4)
34. Worldwide workers group (abbr.)
35. Fantasy (Fr.)
36. Time for les grandes vacances
37. College building
38. "Thou hast been in ____ the garden of God" (Ezekiel 28:13)
39. "Evening ____" (former TV show)
41. Part of a circle (abbr.)
43. Tithe fraction
46. Park ____ (neighborhood in Brooklyn, NY)
50. ____ Canal
52. "____ his marvellous works...his wonders" (1 Chronicles 16:12)
54. Circuit
55. Mouths
56. On; upon (prefix)
57. ____ room
58. Blemish
59. Actress Sandra

DOWN

1. ____ Hill, where Paul spoke in Athens
2. Assist
3. City on the Arno River
4. "The ____ that smote the image became a great mountain" (Daniel 2:35)
5. "The words of his mouth were smoother than butter, but ____ was in his heart" (Psalm 55:21)
6. Mythological god of war
7. Babylonian conqueror
8. "Smite...and destroy all the children of ____" (Numbers 24:17)
9. "The children of Israel...cannot be ____ nor numbered" (Hosea 1:10)
10. "Men have not heard, nor perceived by the ____" (Isaiah 64:4)
11. Sea bird
16. "Ye pay ____ of mint and anise" (Matthew 23:23)
20. Furniture wood
22. "They...were forbidden of the Holy Ghost to preach the word in ____" (Acts 16:6)
24. Church part
25. Observed
26. Mirrors
27. Orpah's sister-in-law
28. "From the beginning of the ____ God made them male and female" (Mark 10:6)

30. ____ at ease
31. "They should not worship devils and idols of ____" (Revelation 9:20)
35. King's domain
37. Little red one
40. "Thou hast laid me in the lowest pit...in the ____" (Psalm 88:6)
42. To cause to be (suffix, Brit.)
44. "Doth he thank that servant...? I ____ not" (Luke 17:9)
45. Wife of Zeus
47. Grandfather of David
48. Cartoon character LePew
49. Pennsylvania city

50. Small-town America street
51. ____ v. Wade
53. "They ____ my path, they set forward my calamity" (Job 30:13)

PUZZLE 42

ACROSS

1. Wrath
4. Send out
8. "They made a calf...and offered sacrifice unto the ____" (Acts 7:41)
12. From or to a distance (prefix)
13. "He maketh the storm a ____" (Psalm 107:29)
14. Bog
15. He thought Hannah had been drinking
16. Bold alternative
17. Disobey a road sign
18. "Do good to them that ____ you" (Matthew 5:44)
20. Lady of Spain, perhaps (abbr.)
21. "In thee, O Lord, do I put my ____" (Psalm 71:1)
23. "____ God in the day of visitation" (1 Peter 2:12)
27. Clarifying abbr.
28. From here one has a bird's-eye view
30. Ripped apart (arch.)
31. Feminine name
33. "There is a ____, the streams whereof shall make glad" (Psalm 46:4)
35. Little lamb's cry
36. Land measure
38. AKA Cephas
40. Title of respect (abbr.)
41. What Demetrius the silversmith made (Acts 19:24)
43. Children of the vindicated Job: ____ sons and three daughters
44. Number of pieces of silver belonging to the woman in the parable of the lost coin
45. Cash cow (abbr.)
46. Isle of ____, in the English Channel
49. Arafat's assoc.
50. Not a lot
53. Buffalo's lake
54. ____ *Window* (Hitchcock film)
55. Before
56. Coffin
57. "____ it even to the foundation thereof" (Psalm 137:7)
58. Tribe of Israel

DOWN

1. Believer in (suffix)
2. Cousin, e.g.
3. U.S. statesman Root
4. "I will ____ you abroad among the nations" (Nethemiah 1:8)
5. Actor Alan
6. "They angered him... so that it went ____ with Moses" (Psalm 106:32)
7. Britain's John Major, once (abbr.)
8. "That I may ____ unto you some spiritual gift" (Romans 1:11)
9. "I must ____ in this land" (Deuteronomy 4:22)
10. Mine find
11. What Fred Astaire did?
17. Hit's inits.
19. Good king of Judah
20. Storm hazard
21. Son of Japheth (Genesis 10:2)
22. Toothbrush brand
23. "What ___ ?"
24. The Great ____ ____ (name for God)
25. "For he knoweth our ___; he remembereth that we are dust" (Psalm 103:14)

26. Pine
29. What sour grapes do, hopefully
32. To blunder
34. "I will ____ health unto thee" (Jeremiah 30:17)
37. One or the other
39. Jerky movement during sleep (abbr.)
42. "I will spread my ____ upon them" (Hosea 7:12)
45. Exclamation of pity
46. Sticky trap
47. Son of Bela (1 Chronicles 7:7)
48. Give (Scot.)
49. Legume

50. "I have ____ you with milk" (1 Corinthians 3:2)
51. Tide competitor
52. Benign skin tumor
54. B & O, e.g.

PUZZLE 43

ACROSS

1. "The ____ trees of the wheels were joined to the base" (1 Kings 7:32)
5. Ingredient in some cereals
9. Father of Kish (1 Samuel 9:1)
10. "____ up a child in the way he should go" (Proverbs 22:6)
12. Achieve success (colloq.)
13. "Mount Sion, which is ____" (Deuteronomy 4:48)
15. Fuss
16. Let go, not so nicely
18. Greek letter
19. Utility org. for noncity dwellers
20. Main rooms of ancient Roman house
22. Poetic contraction
23. Support one's alma mater
25. Job requirements
27. Stack or rack
29. "Ye shall go out with joy and be ____ forth with peace" (Isaiah 55:12)
30. Side and back, to name two
34. Narrow, deep pass
38. The style of (suffix)
39. Accustomed oneself, with "into"
41. Son of Benjamin (Genesis 46:21)
42. Push, and even shove
43. Inhabitant, e.g. (abbr.)
44. "Ye shall be hated of all ____" (Matthew 10:22)
45. Hope for all generations: Jesus has ____ from the dead!
48. Saturated with liquid, with "up"
51. "Laying up in ____ for themselves a good foundation" (1 Timothy 6:19)
52. "For we which have believed do ____ into rest" (Hebrews 4:3)
53. Taken to court
54. "Call ye upon him while he is ____" (Isaiah 55:6)

DOWN

1. Europe, in particular, to Americans
2. Hours in the day, to a centurion
3. O.T. book
4. "For Jacob my servant's sake, and Israel mine ____" (Isaiah 45:4)
5. Brother of Caleb (Joshua 15:17)
6. Linking verb
7. Black liquid
8. Tribe of Israel
9. Actress Eve
11. "But I will shew thee that which is ____ in the scripture" (Daniel 10:21)
12. River in Switzerland
14. Fashion designer Byron
17. Son of Benjamin (Genesis 46:21)
20. "Now it is high time to ____… now is our salvation nearer" (Romans 13:11)
21. "____ you ways and your doings" (Jeremiah 7:3)
24. Exclamation of surprise
26. Fuss
28. Ached
30. Watery animal fluid (pl.)
31. Alexander and others
32. Forgives; pardons
33. Compass dir.
35. "The third part of an hin of oil to ____ with the fine flour" (Ezekiel 46:14)
36. "Be of good ___; I have overcome the world" (John 16:33)

37. "Naphtali is a ____ let loose"
(Genesis 49:21)
40. Industrial center in Germany
46. French coin
47. Before
49. "As the body is ____, and hath
many members"
(1 Corinthians 12:12)
50. School org.

PUZZLE 44

ACROSS

1. Sinful
4. "And the Spirit and the ____ say, Come" (Revelation 22:17)
9. Word in many ranch names
12. On the outside (prefix)
13. To let slacken
14. Put on ____ (postpone)
15. Rebelled against
17. Convalesced
19. Friendly and Flintstone
21. "Shall I come unto you with a ____, or in love" (1 Corinthians 4:21)
22. "I give unto you power to ____ on serpents" (Luke 10:19)
24. "The labour of the righteous ____ to life" (Proverbs 10:16)
28. Actor William
29. Ms. Moreno
30. "As it was in the days of ____" (Luke 17:26)
31. Product safety inits.
32. "There was a rainbow...in sight like unto an ____" (Revelation 4:3)
35. Western state (abbr.)
36. NYC opera house
38. "Ye shall eat neither bread nor parched corn, nor green ____" (Leviticus 23:14)
39. Protest
41. Kind of alphabet
43. Dispatches
44. Requirement for college (abbr.)
45. Provides sketchy information
47. Spice rack spice
50. Like a mule, supposedly
53. Miner's pay dirt
54. "Neither let us ____ Christ, as some of them" (1 Corinthians 10:9)
56. Actor Louis
57. ____ & breakfast
58. "Foxes have ____" (Luke 9:58)
59. Oolong, for one

DOWN

1. "I remember thee upon my ____" (Psalm 63:6)
2. Mirror
3. "Who maketh thee to ____ from another?" (1 Corinthians 4:7)
4. To be fruitful
5. Comedian Foxx
6. Within; toward (prefix)
7. "Mine eye also is ____ by reason of sorrow" (Job 17:7)
8. "The ____ God is thy refuge" (Deuteronomy 33:27)
9. Implored (arch.)
10. Team's "winningest" pitcher
11. ____ Sea
16. Consumed with anger
18. Where Cain dwelled: land of ___
20. "I was dumb with silence...and my sorrow was ____" (Psalm 39:2)
22. Tom of Ringling Bros. fame
23. "I will make thee ____ over many things" (Matthew 25:21)
25. Greek letters
26. Namely (2 words)
27. Gives new life, as Jesus Christ does
29. Camino ___
33. "My soul ____ for heaviness" (Psalm 119:28)

34. "They that will be rich fall...into many...lusts, which ____ men in destruction" (1 Timothy 6:9)
37. "When the ruler of the feast had ____ the water that was made wine" (John 2:9)
40. Say okay
42. "____ ____ [2 words] with you, saith the Lord" (Haggai 1:13)
43. Book divisions
46. On cowboy's saddle checklist
47. ____ Hill, San Francisco
48. Office or function (suffix)
49. Neon competitor
51. Grain
52. KJV assent
55. Metric measure (abbr.)

PUZZLE 45

ACROSS

1. Horned mammal, often mentioned in the Bible
4. Son of (Hebrew)
7. ____ of Man
10. Tizzy
11. Compass pt.
12. One from Tarsus
14. "The younger son...____ his substance with riotous living" (Luke 15:13)
16. "Aaron and ____ stayed up his hands" (Exodus 17:12)
17. Exclamation of relief
19. Many moons
20. Mother ____
21. Jeanne d'Arc, for one (abbr.)
22. Hive dweller
24. "Exalt him that is ____" (Ezekiel 21:26)
25. To dam up
26. Simile syntax
27. "____ thou on my right hand" (Mark 12:36)
28. Legume
29. ____ eagle (skating stunt)
32. Almost
35. Cereal grain
36. Baseball great Drysdale
37. That is (abbr.)
38. "What do ye, loosing the ____" (Mark 11:5)
40. "Ye are grown ____ as the heifer at grass" (Jeremiah 50:11)
41. Appeal
43. Hole-making device
44. Put down
45. Nemesis, certainly
46. Exist
47. Outward appearance
48. "Do I seek to ____men?" (Galatians 1:10)
51. "____ thyself now with majesty and excellency" (Job 40:10)
53. ____ Dolorosa
54. "All the rivers ____ unto the sea" (Ecclesiastes 1:7)
55. Consumed
56. "Go to the ____, thou sluggard" (Proverbs 6:6)
57. Mamie Eisenhower, ____ Dowd

DOWN

1. Unrefined
2. Michigan town near Grand Rapids
3. Brother of Miriam
4. Has ____
5. Kind of game
6. Quadrant in D.C.
7. "All the women...in wisdom ____ goats' hair" (Exodus 35:26)
8. Paddle
9. Greek letter
13. Better than never
15. Big ____: circus site
16. "____ thee two tables of stone" (Exodus 34:1)
18. It gets let down
20. Kind of plate
21. "We have seen his ____ in the east" (Matthew 2:2)
22. "And there ____ light" (Genesis 1:3)
23. Slithering one
24. Put a ____ on it
25. Galilee, for one
27. Made a lap
28. Do a scribe's work

30. Bagel's basic kin
31. "And he said unto me, Take it, and _____ it up" (Revelation 10:9)
32. Slangy negative
33. "I speak the truth in Christ and _____ not" (1 Timothy 2:7)
34. Yes, to King James
36. "The _____ of the Lord is at hand" (Joel 1:15)
38. NYC sight
39. "One _____ five hundred pence, and the other fifty" (Luke 7:41)
40. _____ East
41. "Annabel Lee" poet

42. "Go ye and _____ what that meaneth" (Matthew 9:13)
44. Word in Valley Girl's vocabulary
45. Slipper, for example
47. Form of legislation
48. Bobby, for one
49. Feminine nickname
50. Compass pt.
52. Apiece (abbr.)
53. One of the thirteen colonies (abbr.)

PUZZLE 46

ACROSS

1. ____ Colonies, in eastern Iowa
6. Balmy weekend sky sight (pl.)
11. "I will bring the third part through the fire and will ____ them" (Zechariah 13:9)
13. Reason for saying "excuse me"
14. Popular NYC art museum, for short
15. Org. that includes Braves but not Indians
16. Pacific state (abbr.)
17. Pitcher's stat.
18. Mulberry, for one (abbr.)
19. Recover from the attic? (2 words)
22. Masculine nickname
23. "And ____ were the more added to the Lord" (Acts 5:14)
25. Prohibits
27. Compass pt.
28. Site of Miami University
31. Door sign
32. "Open ___"
33. Pictured on highway sign
34. Sporty Ford model
37. Mimic
38. "Ye became ____ of us and of the Lord" (1 Thessalonians 1:6)
41. Hospital abbr.
43. Desired deeply
44. Kind of M.D.
46. Bygone automobile
48. Article
49. Sound of hesitation
50. Library section (abbr.)
51. "Thou shalt heap coals of fire upon his head, and the Lord shall ____ thee" (Proverbs 25:22)
53. Missouri and Ohio
55. Mohair measure
56. "The way of an ____ in the air" (Proverbs 30:19)

DOWN

1. "Underneath are the everlasting ____" (Deuteronomy 33:27)
2. Track competition
3. Astern
4. Metal in a 5-ct. piece
5. Abolish
6. Butter, for one
7. Common abbr.
8. Summer wear, for short
9. Old Testament scribe
10. "____ the law among my disciples" (Isaiah 8:16)
12. Feminine nickname
13. More pointed than push
19. "There is one lawgiver, who is able to save and to ____" (James 4:12)
20. "Abram had dwelt ____ years in the land" (Genesis 16:3)
21. "A ____ man soweth strife" (Proverbs 16:28)
23. Lawyer's homework
24. "King Solomon made a navy of ____" (1 Kings 9:26)
25. "Arise, take up thy ____, and go" (Matthew 9:6)
26. Let go (colloq.)
29. Chemical suffix
30. Poetic contraction
34. Pituitary, for one
35. Rocky hill
36. Land ____
39. "Now ____ a parable of the fig tree" (Matthew 24:32)
40. Strange
41. Answers incorrectly

42. Exude fumes
44. "That ____" (one-time TV sitcom)
45. Assume a position
47. Assume a mortgage, for example
50. "Let his children be continually vagabonds, and ____" (Psalm 109:10)
52. "I have given into thy hand the king of ____" (Joshua 8:1)
54. Site of Jamestown (abbr.)

PUZZLE 47

ACROSS

1. Poetic contraction
4. "The ____ of the mountains is his pasture" (Job 39:8)
9. ____ fried
12. Linking verb
13. "The ____ of Egypt shall be moved" (Isaiah 19:1)
14. Inlet
15. "Behold a man gluttonous...a ____ of publicans and sinners" (Matthew 11:19)
17. "Charity...is not ____ provoked, thinketh no evil" (1 Corinthians 13:4, 5)
19. Joke
20. Brownish gray
21. Liturgical season that coincides with spring
23. ____ sum (Chinese dumplings)
24. Man, for example
27. Printer's measures
28. "Every ____ that a man doeth is without the body" (1 Corinthians 6:18)
29. "When thou prayest, ____ into thy closet" (Matthew 6:6)
30. ____ out (tennis term)
31. "The ____ went before, the players on instruments followed" (Psalm 68:25)
33. Movie rating
34. "Pay that which thou hast ____" (Ecclesiastes 5:4)
36. Singing syllable
37. About
38. Pitcher
39. James Herriot, for short
40. Driven group
41. "But ____ foolish questions, and genealogies" (Titus 3:9)

43. Blue
44. "Pharaoh was wroth...against the chief of the ____" (Genesis 40:2)
46. "The wicked shall be ____ in darkness" (1 Samuel 2:9)
49. Be in debt
50. "Aeneas, which had kept his bed ____ years" (Acts 9:33)
52. Years and years
53. Skin tumor
54. Grown-up gadgets, collectively
55. Ran into

DOWN

1. Boor
2. Stumble
3. Royal eras
4. American humorist Lardner
5. "____ to your faith virtue" (2 Peter 1:5)
6. Negative
7. Shine like the sun
8. More hirsute son of Isaac
9. "Jesus, made an high ____ for ever" (Hebrews 6:20)
10. Fare poorly
11. Negative, old style
16. Sup
18. Twirls
20. Got goosebumps
21. Make a getaway
22. "He shall surely ____ her to be his wife" (Exodus 22:16)
23. Noise level
25. Disdained individual, in Bible times
26. Energy unit
28. Caesar
29. TV series
31. "If any man ____ me, let him follow me" (John 12:26)

32. "Where wilt thou that we prepare for thee to _____ the passover?" (Matthew 26:17)
35. "O Lucifer...which didst _____ the nations" (Isaiah 14:12)
37. "I will _____ them from death" (Hosea 13:14)
39. Call on
40. Masculine nickname
42. Swedish coin
43. Tends to tots, tersely
44. Half a canine call
45. Reverence
46. Less than, with "of"

47. "As it was in the days of _____" (Luke 17:26)
48. Terminator, in a way (abbr.)
51. Matthew 28:19 verb

PUZZLE **48**

ACROSS

1. "And falling into a place where two ____ met, they ran the ship aground" (Acts 27:41)
5. Father of Adoniram (1 Kings 4:6)
9. Linking verb
12. Yen
13. "I will fasten him as a ____ in a sure place" (Isaiah 22:23)
14. "La ____" (Debussy composition)
15. Tear
16. "And David saith, Let their table be made a...____" (Romans 11:9)
17. Certain vegetable serving
18. Extraordinary, in a way
20. "She layeth her ____ to the spindle" (Proverbs 31:19)
22. "If ye be reproached for the name of Christ, ____ are ye" (1 Peter 4:14)
24. Flap
25. Like a New York minute (abbr.)
26. At ____
29. Watch ___
33. Is supine
35. Cotton ___
36. Genus of the lily family
37. "My father did ____ you with a heavy yoke" (1 Kings 12:11)
38. Remove bobby pins
40. ____ the line
41. Poetic before
43. Rethink and revise
45. "He will not always ____: neither will he keep his anger" (Psalm 103:9)
48. It's sometimes glaring
50. "Thy word have I ____ in mine heart" (Psalm 119:11)
51. Kind of light or line

53. Tribe of Israel
56. Natural combination of minerals
57. Kilmer subject
58. And others (abbr.)
59. Pod dweller
60. "O ____ out thy light and thy truth" (Psalm 43:3)
61. Synagogue

DOWN

1. Polite title
2. Greek letter
3. "Behold, now is the ____ time; behold, now is the day of salvation" (2 Corinthians 6:2)
4. "We thy people and ____ of thy pasture" (Psalm 79:13)
5. Kind of hero
6. "John ____ witness of him" (John 1:15)
7. Circle part (abbr.)
8. Wave or ray
9. So be it
10. "They could not ____ the writing" (Daniel 5:8)
11. Solomon writes that whoever refuses reproof ___
19. Pastrami on ____ (deli order)
21. "____ Father, all things are possible" (Mark 14:36)
22. "I...have the keys of ____ and of death" (Revelation 1:18)
23. Continent
24. Mind the store
27. Marked by chills
28. "Where ____ abounded, grace did much more" (Romans 5:20)
30. "The law of the Medes and Persians, which ____ not" (Daniel 6:8)
31. High time

32. "A prophet mighty in _____ and word" (Luke 24:19)
34. Kind of money
39. Boathouse sight
42. Musical notations
44. Underground workers
45. Kind of house
46. "The labourer is worthy of his _____" (Luke 10:7)
47. Notion
48. "All the trees of _____, the choice and best of Lebanon" (Ezekiel 31:16)
49. "A bruised _____ shall he not break" (Matthew 12:20)
52. Wrath
54. Hebrew letter
55. Under the weather

PUZZLE 49

ACROSS

1. "What ____ I am afraid, I will trust in thee" (Psalm 56:3)
5. "They cast ____, that is, the lot, before Haman" (Esther 3:7)
8. It's not exactly red
12. In the near future (arch.)
13. Gobbled up
14. First two words in Key's composition
15. "Help thou mine ____" (Mark 9:24)
17. *Au* ____ (teenaged helper)
18. Relieve
19. Filled with evil desires, as a heart
21. Synonym for scow
24. Toward the sheltered side
25. "____ them that have the rule over you" (Hebrews 13:17)
26. "Thou hast ____ me when I was in distress" (Psalm 4:1)
30. Legal object
31. Michael, for one
32. Poem
33. "Yea, I ____ unto you, and... none of you that convinced Job" (Job 32:12)
35. Zone
36. Beverages
37. Squander
38. Cyrus was the king of ____ (Ezra 3:7)
41. One who hisses
42. Skirt feature
43. "Be sober, be ____" (1 Peter 5:8)
48. Melita, for one
49. Natural mineral
50. Day before (pl.)
51. Samuel, to some
52. See ____

53. Want no more

DOWN

1. Greek letter
2. Holiday, for one
3. Multitude
4. Strength
5. Receipt word
6. Western Native American
7. What the watchful waiter did?
8. Mines found on Cyprus
9. Dweller in the land of Seir, the country of Edom (Genesis 32:3)
10. Depilatory brand
11. Seaport in Lebanon
16. Recline
20. Repast
21. Fierce wind of the Adriatic
22. Aid's ally
23. What's left
24. Heavenly beings (Fr.)
26. Earnest attempt
27. Blood and guts
28. Utopia
29. "If we be ____ with Christ...we shall also live with him" (Romans 6:8)
31. Girl's nickname
34. Resurrection day
35. "A word fitly spoken is like ____ of gold" (Proverbs 25:11)
37. Supplemental income (abbr.)
38. Greek letters
39. Word in a threat
40. Stir up
41. Long in the tooth
44. Anger
45. Actress Gardner
46. Fish trap
47. Double this for (perhaps) fatal flier

1 2 3 4 5 6 7 8 9 10 11
12 13 14
15 16 17
18 19 20
21 22 23 24
25 26 27 28 29
30 31 32
33 34 35
36 37
38 39 40 41
42 43 44 45 46 47
48 49 50
51 52 53

ACROSS

1. Mentor to Samuel
4. "Sir, we would see ____" (John 12:21)
9. Judicial sentence
12. Benign skin tumor
13. City of Hadad (Genesis 36:35)
14. "Out of whose womb came the ___?" (Job 38:29)
15. Apiece (abbr.)
16. Sign
17. ____ of Melchisedec (Hebrews 7:11)
19. "I was ____ in iniquity" (Psalm 51:5)
21. Ask what might have been
22. French possessive pronoun
23. Said goodnight
27. Without a nom or a nom de plume (abbr.)
29. "Simon Peter...went into the sepulchre, and seeth the ____ clothes" (John 20:6)
30. Bible language (abbr.)
31. ___-oni (Rachel's son)
32. Grace
33. Function
34. Son of Judah (Genesis 38:6)
35. Already sold
36. Played a tuba?
37. "Men of low degree...and men of high degree...are altogether ____ than vanity" (Psalm 62:9)
39. One one-thousandth of an inch
40. Ancient Hebrew liquid measure
41. "Dost thou still ____ thine integrity?" (Job 2:9)
44. "I lay in Sion a chief corner ____" (1 Peter 2:6)
46. "Ye ____ men with burdens grievous" (Luke 11:46)
47. Concerning
48. French possessive pronoun
49. "A man's wisdom maketh his face to ____" (Ecclesiastes 8:1)
51. Parts of a yr.
52. Actor Morita
53. Pursues, as the truth
54. "Go to the ____, thou sluggard" (Proverbs 6:6)

DOWN

1. Jacob gave Esau 200 ____ and 20 rams (Genesis 32:13-14)
2. Mother of Dinah
3. Hoosier state (abbr.)
4. Son of Zebedee, and disciple of Jesus
5. Tied
6. "Be ye angry, and ____ not" (Ephesians 4:26)
7. State of Salt Lake (abbr.)
8. "For the bed is ____ than that a man can stretch himself on it" (Isaiah 28:20)
9. New Jersey college
10. Fast point, in tennis
11. ____ your instructions
16. ____ sesame
18. "The ____ of that house was great" (Luke 6:49)
20. Son of Manasseh, king of Judah (2 Kings 21:18)
23. Ohio, for one
24. "John also was baptizing in ____" (John 3:23)
25. "Woe to them that are at ____ in Zion" (Amos 6:1)
26. Popular female fictional detective
27. Brother of Seth
28. Father of Salathiel (Luke 3:27)

29. Gennesaret, for one
32. "Let your soul delight itself in ____" (Isaiah 55:2)
33. Father of Arah (1 Chronicles 7:39)
35. Willowy
36. "If ye ____ and devour one another, take heed" (Galatians 5:15)
38. Holy ___
39. Overtakers of Babylon
41. Sergeant, for example
42. ____ horse
43. Aerie
44. Brand of automobile oil

45. Orange Pekoe, for example
46. "The highways ____ waste, the wayfaring man ceaseth" (Isaiah 33:8)
50. Pronoun
51. Sturbridge state (abbr.)

ANSWERS

Collection # 11

Puzzle 1

	W	O	R	L	D	S						S	G		
	A	R	I	A			A	B	I		I	L	K	S	
	S	A	T	I	A	T	E	D				M	A	S	T
			E	S	T				H	O	S				
	M	A	S	H		I	N	C	E	N	S	E	D		
	I	F			S	T	E	A	L			G	O		
	C	O		R	A	B	B	I			B	Y			
	A	R		S	A	L	A			W	E	P	T		
	H	E	A	P		T	O	P	H	E	T	H			
		M	U	L	E		W	E	A	R					
	D	A	M	N	A	B	L	E		T	A	R	E		
	E	X	O		L	A	I	T	Y			O	R		
	W	E	N		A	L	P	H	A			E	E		

Puzzle 2

	E	H	I		O	R	P	A	H			M	E	
	H	E	N		R	O	U	S	E		S	A	Y	
	U	Z		T	A	B	L	E		H	I	D	E	
	D	E	B	A	T	E		R	U	I	N	E	D	
		K	E	R	O	S		S	E	A				
	W	I	S	E	R		K	E	L	I	T	A		
	E	A	T		A	B	S			O	R			
	T	H	I	R	S	T	Y		H	U	K	O	K	
	R	I	E		T	I	R	E						
	B	E		S	I	N	G	I	N	G				
	C	O	N	S	I	D	E	R		E	L	O	N	
	O	R	E		N	E	B	A	T		A	S	A	
	L	O	W		G	N	A	S	H		H	E	W	

Puzzle 3

	R	T	E		K	I	S	H	I			H	O	
	A	R	A		O	T	H	E	R		J	A	M	
	S	O		W	H	E	E	L		G	A	T	E	
	H	U	P	H	A	M		M	A	N	N	E	R	
		B	O	A	T	S		P	A	N				
	S	L	O	T	H		A	T	T	A	I	N		
	E	E	R		I	R	S			C	O			
	A	S	E	N	A	T	H		O	W	N	E	R	
		R	O	B		A	B	I	A					
		T	I		A	N	A	N	I	A	S			
	B	R	E	E	D	I	N	G		D	O	S	T	
	E	A	R		A	R	E	L	I		T	I	E	
	E	W	E		N	A	M	E	S		H	A	P	

Puzzle 4

		Q	U	A	K	E		T	E	A	C	H	
	S	U	P	P	E	R		H	A	S	H	E	M
	H	E		T	E	R	R	O	R	S		L	O
	E	N		P	E	A	R	S			K	I	
	D	C	C		T	E	N			W	A	S	
	S	H	E	L	A	H		S	P	I	R	I	T
		A	I	R			U	S	E				
	J	A	S	P	E	R		E	L	A	S	A	H
	A	T	E		H	A	S			T	H	E	
	S	A		H	O	S	T	S			I	S	
	O	R		G	O	D	H	E	A	D		M	E
	N	A	T	U	R	E		E	L	I	D	A	D
		H	O	R	N	S		M	A	D	O	N	

Puzzle 5

Row 1: SIAHA · ALOOF
Row 2: CITIES · HANNAH
Row 3: AS · MET · YE · IE
Row 4: LEAVENED · ERR
Row 5: ARBA · AMA · EYED
Row 6: HAIL · TATTLERS
Row 7: SUAH · EPI
Row 8: EPHER · HAB
Row 9: AHASAI · SORER
Row 10: SUIT · TITHE · TO
Row 11: ER · BASHAN · HE
Row 12: DANIEL · AGABUS
Row 13: HONEY · NEIEL

Puzzle 6

Row 1: HINES · HEAPS
Row 2: BOTTLE · OWNETH
Row 3: OR · HANDLED · AI
Row 4: AR · MAIDS · IR
Row 5: ROM · AGE · ARA
Row 6: DRIETH · NAHASH
Row 7: DRS · PAR
Row 8: SEED · STROKE
Row 9: BAT · AHA · NON
Row 10: AM · SMOTE · HO
Row 11: RI · SANDALS · AS
Row 12: STALE · NAHATH
Row 13: SALAD · SHETH

Puzzle 7

Row 1: KINGLY · JAAKAN
Row 2: IT · NEEDETH · SO
Row 3: SEAT · ISAIAH
Row 4: DTS · SIDON
Row 5: UZ · AHA · AS
Row 6: SEPHAR · HAGABA
Row 7: EPHER · TIDAL
Row 8: SHIMMA · BENONI
Row 9: TI · HAI · AM
Row 10: ISA · STRAW
Row 11: SNUB · ATONES
Row 12: OP · CLOSEST · HE
Row 13: GATHER · RESTED

Puzzle 8

Row 1: HONOR · STEPS
Row 2: BENONI · HOPETH
Row 3: UZ · RESHEPH · AI
Row 4: KI · SEALS · RR
Row 5: KOA · SIA · ARA
Row 6: INFANT · HERESH
Row 7: ORO · RAN
Row 8: ROOTED · SIMONS
Row 9: ART · ROE · NEH
Row 10: HA · HOBAH · TO
Row 11: AT · SOPATER · HE
Row 12: BOWELS · ERITES
Row 13: READY · DEBIR

Puzzle 9

Row 1: AM · VISIT · AN
Row 2: ARAN · OTHNI · HO
Row 3: PARADISE · WET
Row 4: OH · MIC · AC · ARE
Row 5: DEMETRIUS
Row 6: ONE · SO · ER · SA
Row 7: BENO · OLIVES
Row 8: AR · IS · SN · OAK
Row 9: SLIME · PAWS
Row 10: RIE · AI · EZ · OF
Row 11: IRA · NAHAMANI
Row 12: BITHYNIA · OMER
Row 13: SEEING · NED

Puzzle 10

Row 1: SOLES · OZIAS
Row 2: KOHATH · NERIAH
Row 3: ED · MAASIAI · PE
Row 4: NO · MAHOL · HE
Row 5: AMI · PEN · OIL
Row 6: NAMETH · STAIRS
Row 7: NAH · OWL
Row 8: SEARED · SPEECH
Row 9: ASH · EST · DOE
Row 10: TH · FAIRS · OR
Row 11: AT · DALAIAH · LO
Row 12: NOTICE · FLOWED
Row 13: NIGER · EARED

Puzzle 11

Puzzle 12

Puzzle 13

Puzzle 14

Puzzle 15

Puzzle 16

Puzzle 17

Puzzle 18

Puzzle 19

Puzzle 20

Puzzle 21

Puzzle 22

Puzzle 23

```
S O B . P I P E . S W A T
O R A . A T E R . P A V E
P E R . R E A R . E R I E
. . N O A M . A M E N D S
S T A I D . E N I D . . .
T A B L E . A D D . G O A
A L A S . I T S . S L I P
Y E S . N N E . H E E L S
. . J O H N . E R A S E .
A D H E R E . K E E N . .
M I A S . R A I D . I R E
E C R U . I D L E . N O N
N E T S . T E N D . G O D
```

Puzzle 24

```
C A . S E B A . S H A M E
U R . S T E M . L I N E N
R E S . A T . W O R D . .
B A T T L E . A W E . A I
S . A R . A S . S A N D .
. R E T E S T . T H E E .
T E . O N S E T . . M A .
O B E D . M E D I U M . .
M E N E . I S . S O R T .
E D . S A T . D E E P E R
. T I N Y . R A . S P A .
S H A R E . H O R N . A D
S T R E W . A P S E . Y E
```

Puzzle 25

```
D A M . H O R S E . B I D
O B E Y . G A L L . U T E
M E L E E . H A Z E R I M
. T A L L . Y A R N S . .
G R I S L E D . B A T . .
R A N T . A R B A S . B Y
E G G . A V O I D . B E E
W E . C R E W S . B L E W
. M A R . N O T I O N S .
. D A V I D . N E T S . .
F O R E V E R . N E S T S
E R R . E B E R . S O R E
W A Y . S T O W S . M A T
```

Puzzle 26

```
B A R A K . H A G G I A H
L . O D E S . S E E T H E
A H . D E E P . M E . E A
R I M . P L O W S . F A R
E N O S . A T E . D A R K
. D A T A . E . H I . T E
C . B E G I N N I N G . N
U H . R E . T . S E R F .
N O O N . P A W . D O E R
C R Y . C I T E S . W E E
E N . G O . E S A U . T I
D E S E R T . T U R N . N
E T E R N A L . L I O N S
```

Puzzle 27

```
R E P . A B E A M . S T A
O E R . S E R V E . P A W
B R O T H E R . S P I N E
. P E E P . T S A R . . .
G A H A R . F A I R E S T
A H E M . G E R A . T O .
A L T . E L I A S . J A W
S A . T O S H . T U R N .
H I G H E S T . N E S T S
. H E R S . G O A T . . .
S T E R N . S O R R O W S
E O N . A N I A M . N O E
W E T . L O R D S . E N E
```

Puzzle 28

```
E T C H . T I S . O B O E
N R A . P A S T E . A L L
D I S T A L . U G A N D A
. C H A L C E D O N Y . M
. K E N . N . T A P . . .
A S S . A G A T E . N A G
I T . D I A M O N D . N O
M E N . D R E G S . B A G
. R I O . L . L A T . . .
N . C H R Y S O L Y T E .
A T E M P O . P U E B L O
N I L . H Y R A X . O A R
O N Y X . O I L . L Y S E
```

Puzzle 29

S	H	Y		D	A	S	H		S	P	O	T

Crossword grid — Puzzle 29:
Row 1: S H Y · D A S H · S P O T
Row 2: L E E · A C H E · N O A H
Row 3: I A · D I N E · D A I R Y
Row 4: P R A I S E · H I P S ·
Row 5: · W R Y · B E S P E A K
Row 6: S U E T · M E R C Y · S I
Row 7: O L D · B A A L S · G I N
Row 8: A N · V E N U S · B R A D
Row 9: P A T I E N T · G E E ·
Row 10: · O R C A · P R A Y E R
Row 11: F A I T H · C A E N · D O
Row 12: L U L U · L O V E · W E D
Row 13: T O · E · O P E N · O N E

Puzzle 30

Crossword grid — Puzzle 30:
Row 1: S U S A · C R A B · R U N
Row 2: S P E D · Z O B A · O N E
Row 3: E S A U · A B E L · A D O
Row 4: · L O R E · A A R O N
Row 5: A M I T Y · S A X
Row 6: J E R · S A L E M · M I O
Row 7: A D A M · B I T · B O T H
Row 8: R E N · B E T H L E H E M
Row 9: O U T · A T O M S
Row 10: C H U R N · S A S H
Row 11: H A G · D E E P · A C T S
Row 12: I L L · L O N E · N O A H
Row 13: P L Y · E N D S · Y O R E

Puzzle 31

Crossword grid — Puzzle 31:
Row 1: R E A M · C O W · H O P E
Row 2: I D D O · O R O · E N O S
Row 3: D E A R · R A N · W E R E
Row 4: · T I P · D I E ·
Row 5: L A B A N S · E N R A G E
Row 6: S T E R N E · R E S C U E
Row 7: R A · · H A
Row 8: R I S E U P · T E M A N S
Row 9: N A T U R E · A R E N O T
Row 10: · R U N · B E D ·
Row 11: U N D O · U A R · D O R A
Row 12: R E A P · R T E · L E A H
Row 13: I R M A · Y E T · E R M A

Puzzle 32

Crossword grid — Puzzle 32:
Row 1: B A N C · F I R · E B E D
Row 2: B R I O · U R E · L O V E
Row 3: B O N N · R A N · E D E N
Row 4: N E C R O M A N C E R
Row 5: E A R · M O T
Row 6: L I M I T · F E D · W O N
Row 7: E R A T · R E D · V I N E
Row 8: T A R · H E M · F I N E R
Row 9: S E M · S I N
Row 10: A S T R O L O G E R S
Row 11: A S E A · V A N · G O A D
Row 12: T I L L · E R G · A D I N
Row 13: T A L L · D D S · R E L A

Puzzle 33

Crossword grid — Puzzle 33:
Row 1: C A B S
Row 2: S A M E C H
Row 3: G I N · W H I T
Row 4: M O N · P A I N E D
Row 5: S O N · W A R N · M E R
Row 6: P R E S A G E · S P O I L
Row 7: I T · T I E · S H E · V I
Row 8: N A B A L · C H A R G E R
Row 9: L E V · C H O W · E R A
Row 10: N E P H E W · P E S
Row 11: E P E E · A I R
Row 12: D E S E R T
Row 13: R E N T

Puzzle 34

Crossword grid — Puzzle 34:
Row 1: A R I A · D E B · A C R E
Row 2: S E L F · U R E · T R U E
Row 3: A G E E · R A H · T Y N E
Row 4: A P E · A R E
Row 5: T A R S U S · V A N I T Y
Row 6: A R E T A S · E N D U R E
Row 7: M I S · A A
Row 8: E S T E E M · R E N O I R
Row 9: R E S C U E · A L I E N S
Row 10: C R T · C I S
Row 11: A B E L · H A H · A N N A
Row 12: W E R E · E R E · N E A R
Row 13: E A R S · G A L · S E E M

Puzzle 35

A	L	A	S		P	P	D		N	O	A	H
S	A	R	A		A	L	E		A	N	T	I
A	M	A	T		O	S			B	A	T	S
	P	H	I	L	I	P	P	I	A	N	S	
			S	O	D		A	L	L			
S	W	I	F	T		M	I	L		A	R	I
M	A	N	Y		B	A	R		A	S	I	A
U	S	E		A	R	T		K	N	E	E	L
			P	S	I		S	E	A			
	I	N	H	A	B	I	T	A	N	T	S	
I	D	E	O		E	R	A		I	O	T	A
L	O	R	N		R	A	Y		A	L	A	N
A	L	O	E		Y	E	S		S	A	Y	S

Puzzle 36

A	C	T		S	E	T		P	E	N
S	A	H		L	A	O		E	L	A	N
P	R	E	D	E	S	T	I	N	A	T	E
S	T	R	I	P	E		S	O	T	
		E	N	T		S	O	L	O	M	O	N
C	A	F	E		P	A	L	S		O	L	E
A	G	O	D		L	U	D		A	R	E	A
M	A	R		G	A	T	E		S	T	O	P
P	R	E	S	A	G	E		S	E	A	
		L	I	I		S	E	A	L	E	D
P	R	I	N	C	I	P	A	L	I	T	Y
A	I	D	S		S	A	T		T	R	E
N	A	E		M	T	S		Y	E	S

Puzzle 37

A	N	E	W		A	S	P		N	E	T	S
T	E	R	I		M	I	L		E	L	O	I
T	E	E	D		E	R	A		P	I	R	N
		O	W	N		N	I	H			
S	H	E	W	E	D		K	E	E	P	E	R
C	O	A	S	T	S		S	O	W	E	T	H
O	R	G							T	H	E
R	E	L	I	E	D		A	E	N	E	A	S
E	M	E	R	G	E		S	M	Y	R	N	A
		E	O	N		S	E	M			
M	U	N		I	R	E		P	Y	R	E
A	R	B	A		E	A	R		H	A	I	R
D	I	S	H		D	E	T		M	E	N

Puzzle 38

T	A	P		A	R	A	M		S	A	S	E
E	S	A		L	A	T	U		I	G	O	R
R	I	T		T	I	E	R		N	O	N	E
M	A	R	V	E	L		M	E	A			
		I	E	R		J	U	N	I	P	E	R
S	E	A	T		T	A	R	O		R	A	E
E	R	R		S	A	K	E	S		O	S	E
L	A	C		A	X	E	D		U	S	E	D
A	T	H	A	I	A	H		A	N	E	
		A	L	T		G	U	I	L	T	Y
E	B	E	R		I	B	A	R		Y	E	A
V	E	T	O		O	O	L	A		T	A	R
E	D	E	N		N	O	E	L		E	R	N

Puzzle 39

E	T	C		L	A	I	C		S	A	M	E
B	A	L		A	N	N	O		T	R	U	E
E	R	E		B	O	O	N		R	I	D	E
R	E	A	S	O	N		S	I	A			
		N	E	R		B	U	L	W	A	R	K
E	R		T		F	A	M	E		B	E	E
R	A	W		S	O	R	E	S		U	N	E
A	M	A		A	R	E	S		K	N	O	P
S	A	Y	I	N	G	S		B	I	D	
		M	D	I		M	E	R	A	R	I
A	S	I	A		V	E	E	R		N	O	D
F	L	A	G		E	P	E	E		C	O	D
T	Y	N	E		N	I	T	A		E	T	O

Puzzle 40

G	S	A		S	T	A		P	A	I	N
L	A	S	T		Y	E	N		A	B	L	E
I	D	E	A		R	E	O		I	B	E	X
B	A	R	B		I	N	T	E	R	E	S	T
			I	R	A		H	R			
T	E	N	T	H		J	E	S	U	R	U	N
A	D	A	H		O	R		N	Y	R	O
J	O	N	A	D	A	B		S	C	E	N	T
			O	T		P	O	T			
T	O	G	E	T	H	E	R		I	S	N	T
A	L	I	A		E	P	I		O	K	E
L	I	E	S		N	E	Z		N	O	B	S
C	O	R	E		S	E	E		W	O	E

Puzzle 41

A	L	L		C	O	A	L		B	A	J	A
W	O	E		O	N	C	E		O	N	A	M
E	S	T	A	T	E		B	E	S	I	D	E
		L	E	S	T		N	O	M	E		
D	O	D	O	S		R	O	O	M			
E	V	E	N		B	A	N	C		L	A	D
B	E	N	E	A	R		T	H	R	O	N	E
T	R	Y		M	A	N	O		A	S	T	A
		S	A	Y	S		E	N	T	E	R	
T	E	M	A	N		C	O	C	K			
A	R	E	T	A	S		B	O	S	S	E	S
L	A	L	A		A	B	E	L		I	R	A
E	N		N		M	E	D	E		R	E	D

Puzzle 42

C	A	D			D	O	R		I	R	A	D
A	R	I	B		E	V	E		M	O	L	E
P	E	A	U		M	U	M		R	U	I	N
T	A	L	L		A	M	O	R	I	T	E	S
			W	A	S		V	E				
W	O	M	A	N		H	A	V	I	L	A	H
E	D	A	R		O	I	L		M	E	D	E
S	A	C	K	B	U	T		L	A	V	E	R
		E	T		S	A	G					
C	A	S	T	A	W	A	Y		I	V	A	N
O	M	E	R		A	I	R		N	E	B	O
M	E	N	U		R	O	I		E	R	L	E
A	N	T	E		D	E	A		Y	E	S	

Puzzle 43

A	B	B	A		O	W	N	S		A	D	O
B	A	A	L		F	E	E	T		B	I	N
E	T	E	S		T	E	A	R		O	D	E
T	H	R	O	N	E		R	E	A	D	Y	
		E	N	G		E	N	E	M	Y		
	A	F	T		L	E	T		U	R		
B	A	R		F	O	R		S	I	S		
H	E		E	B	E	R		B	E	N		
A	N	G	E	R		Y	E	A				
	E	N	D	O	R		N	A	T	H	A	N
F	F	A		K	A	L	E		H	A	L	E
R	I	T		E	D	O	M		I	R	M	A
I	T	S		N	O	S	Y		S	E	A	L

Puzzle 44

A	R	T		R	A	F		S	A	R	A
S	O	U	L		A	V	A		P	L	E	B
A	B	B	A		N	E	S		A	L	E	E
		W	I	T	C	H	C	R	A	F	T
H	A	Y	E	S		I	O	E			
L	O	V	E	R		B	O	W		T	H	E
O	M	E	R		T	I	N		S	H	O	W
P	E	R		S	I	T		S	H	I	N	E
		T	I	M		R	A	I	S	E	
B	E	F	O	R	E	T	I	M	E		
A	N	E	W		W	A	S		L	E	N	D
C	O	T	E		A	R	E		D	O	E	R
A	S	E	R		S	O	N		S	O	Y

Puzzle 45

A	G	A	G		S	I	S		A	B	B	E
M	I	L	A		H	A	P		L	A	E	L
P	E	E	R		A	M	A		A	N	T	S
	R	E	M	E	M	B	R	A	N	C	E	
		E	R	E		R	I	D			
A	L	O	N	G		F	O	R		R	A	T
F	E	L	T		N	E	W		J	O	S	E
T	E	D		M	O	W		T	U	B	A	L
		A	R	I		H	E	N			
	M	I	N	I	S	T	E	R	I	N	G	
S	O	N	G		O	A	R		P	I	N	E
H	A	R	E		M	I	O		E	L	A	M
E	B	E	R		E	L	D		R	E	T	S

Puzzle 46

R	E	A	D		R	E	D		P	A	L	E
A	L	I	A		O	R	E		A	G	A	R
M	A	N	Y		M	A	S		I	R	I	S
S	H	U	S	H			P	A	L	A	C	E
		T	I	N		A	I	S			
N	E	B	A	T		T	I	D		R	A	N
A	D	A	R		U	A	R		M	O	V	E
M	E	S		A	N	N		S	O	B	E	R
		E	R	G		C	O	T			
M	O	U	N	T	O	F	O	L	I	V	E	S
E	R	R	S		D	A	R		O	A	T	H
R	A	G	U		L	I	D		N	I	N	A
	N	E	E		Y	R	S		S	N	A	G

Puzzle 47

¹L	O	³Y		⁴A	⁵S	⁶S		⁷C	⁸I	⁹S
¹⁰A	P	E		¹¹L	A	M		¹²S	A	R	A
¹³M	E	R	¹⁴C	I	F	U	L		¹⁵R	A	¹⁶W
¹⁷P	L	E	A	S	E		¹⁸O	¹⁹A	T		
		²⁰F	R	A		²¹C	O	V	E	²²R	²³E	²⁴D
²⁵B	²⁶L	U	E		²⁷M	U	S	E		²⁸E	V	E
²⁹L	A	S	S		³⁰O	R	E		³¹B	E	L	
³²U	T	E		³³D	R	E	D		³⁴H	E	R	E
³⁵R	E	D	³⁶N	E	S	S		³⁷S	E	L	
		³⁸E	E	E		³⁹S	C	A	L	⁴⁰D	⁴¹S
⁴²S	⁴³U	P	P	L	⁴⁴I	C	A	T	I	O	N
⁴⁵I	R	A	S		⁴⁶D	A	R		⁴⁷O	N	O
⁴⁸R	E	L		⁴⁹A	T	E		⁵⁰N	E	W

Puzzle 48

¹I	²D	³A		⁴C	⁵L	⁶A	⁷P		⁸S	⁹T	¹⁰S
¹¹R	E	B		¹²D	E	V	I	L		¹³Y	E	A
¹⁴A	R	I		¹⁵U	N	I		¹⁶E	¹⁷A	R	L	Y
	¹⁸L	E	¹⁹N	T		²⁰L	A	N	I		
²¹L	E	V		²²D	I	S	T	A	N	T
²⁵C	O	N	E		²⁶N	A	V	E	S		²⁷O	H
²⁸A	W	E		²⁹A	R	E		³⁰R	O	E
³¹N	E		³²L	³³A	B	A	N		³⁴D	E	N	Y
³⁵A	R	³⁶T	E	M	A	S		³⁷O	N	E
	³⁸H	E	A	L		³⁹B	⁴⁰A	R	E
⁴¹A	⁴²M	I	S	S		⁴³C	I	S		⁴⁴W	⁴⁵A	⁴⁶N
⁴⁷W	I	N		⁴⁸A	⁴⁹H	I	R	A		⁵⁰E	N	E
⁵¹L	O	G		⁵²S	A	I	D		⁵³D	E	W

Puzzle 49

¹L	²A	³R	⁴A		⁵H	⁶A		⁷C		⁸J	⁹A	¹⁰W
¹¹O	M	E	R		¹²A	L	¹³M	A		¹⁴U	S	A
¹⁵G	I	V	E	¹⁶P	L	A	C	E		¹⁷S	I	R
		¹⁸L	I	V		¹⁹S	²⁰A	T	A	N
²¹F	²²A	²³M	I	N	E		²⁴R	A	N	I
²⁵A	L	A		²⁶S	T	R	I	F	²⁷E
²⁸D	O	²⁹G	S	³⁰E	E	E		³¹M	I	³²R	E
	³³E	N	³⁴A	B	L	E		³⁵E	N	E
	³⁶I	T	E	M		³⁷W	³⁸A	³⁹N	D	E	R
⁴⁰R	⁴¹E	F		⁴²W		⁴²F	I	L	E
⁴³A	L	I		⁴⁴A	⁴⁵V	E	N	G	E	N	⁴⁸O	T
⁴⁹N	O	E		⁵⁰R	A	N	G		⁵¹D	A	R	E
⁵²D	I	D		⁵³E	N	D	S		⁵⁴S	T	A	R

Puzzle 50

¹O	²F	³F		⁴A	⁵L	⁶L		⁷F	⁸O	⁹O	¹⁰T
¹¹T	R	E	¹²S		¹³D	O	A		¹⁴O	M	R	I
¹⁵T	A	T	A		¹⁶O	N	T		¹⁷A	N	C	E
¹⁸O	M	E	R		¹⁹P	E	C	U	L	I	A	R
		²¹E	²²A	T		²³H	E	
²⁴C	²⁵A	²⁶M	P	S		²⁷L	E	A	²⁸D	²⁹E	³⁰R	³¹S
³²P	L	A	T		³³H	O	T		³⁴F	R	I	E
³⁵L	E	B	A	³⁶N	O	N		³⁷A	C	R	E	S
		³⁸O	W		³⁹A	W	L
⁴⁰R	⁴¹E	⁴²M	⁴³E	M	B	⁴⁴E	R		⁴⁵A	⁴⁶G	⁴⁷E	⁴⁸D
⁴⁹I	R	A	D		⁵⁰E	S	O		⁵¹R	A	V	E
⁵²D	A	R	E		⁵³I	T	S		⁵⁴E	V	E	N
⁵⁵E	N	A	N		⁵⁶T	H	E		⁵⁷E	L	S

ANSWERS

Collection # 12

Puzzle 1

Puzzle 2

Puzzle 3

Puzzle 4

Puzzle 5

1 H	2 A	3 I	4 R	5 S		6 R	7 A	8 G	9 E	10 S	
11 S	U	N	S	E	T	12 E	V	A	D	E	13 S
14 P	S	T		15 P	16 U	R	S	E		17 S	A	P
18 O	H			19 P	O	U	R			20 M	I
21 R	A	22 S	23 E		24 O	I	L		25 B	26 A	A	L
27 T	I	M	B	28 E	R		29 T	30 A	L	E	N	T
		31 E	O	N				32 R	E	S	
33 S	34 T	A	N	D	35 S	36 R	E	S	O	37 R	38 T
39 V	E	R	Y		40 U	41 S	E		42 S	P	U	R
43 E	N		44 P	R	I	S	M		45	46 N	E
47 N	O	48 R		49 A	E	R	I	E		50 I	N	N
51 S	N	A	52 I	L	S		53 D	54 A	N	C	E	D
	55 S	W	E	E	T		56 E	L	D	E	R

Puzzle 6

1 O	2 W	3 E		4 W	5 H	6 E	7 A	8 T		9 T	10 A	11 U
12 W	E	N		13 H	E	A	V	I	14 N	E	S	S
15 N	A	T	16 I	O	N	S			17 E	A	S	E
		18 R	E	D			19 S	20 T	R	21 A	W
22 F	I	R	E	S		23 A	N		24 U	S	A
28 O	N		29 A	L	30 A	R	M	S		31 A	W	S
32 C	E	33 N	S	E	R			34 A	35 W	A	K	E S
36 U	S	O		37 E	I	38 T	H	E	R		39 E	N
40 S	S	W		41 P	E	R		42 R	O	43 O	T S
		44 I	S	L	A	M		45 D	46 A	N
47 A	48 R	49 A	M		50 D	E	51 S	I	R	E	52 S
53 H	A	P	P	54 I	55 N	E	S	S		56 S	A
57 A	N	T		58 N	U	R	S	E		59 E	S O

Puzzle 7

1 A	2 R	3 E		4 S	5 E	6 E	7 R	8 S		9 M	10 A	11 N
12 P	A	T		13 T	E	N	E	T		14 E	R	E
15 T	H	E	16 L	O	R	D	L	I	17 V	E	T	H
		18 R	E	P			19 R	O	T
20 H	21 A	N	G	S		22 A	R	I	S	23 E	24 S
25 A	L	A	S		26 C	27 I	T	E	D		28 X	I
29 M	I	L		30 O	I	L	E	D		31 S	I	N
32 A	V		33 E	N	T	E	R		34 B	A	L	K
35 N	36 E	A	T	L	Y			37 S	A	V	E	S
	38 B	U	Y			39 A	I
40 P	41 R	A	I	42 S	43 E	44 T	45 H	E	L	46 O	47 R D
48 H	A	S		49 O	D	O	U	R		50 U	T E
51 I	N	E		52 N	O	T	E	S		53 R	E W

Puzzle 8

1 B	2 E	3 E		4 T	5 O	6 G	7 S		8 P	9 A	10 R	11 T
12 A	S	A		13 A	L	O	E		14 I	L	A	I
15 Y	E	S		16 N	I	L	E		17 A	I	M	S
	18 K	I	19 N	G	O	F	K	20 I	N	G	S
		21 E	E	L	S		22 I	R	O	N
23 W	24 A	S	T	E		25 G	N	U		26 E	27 A
28 A	N	T	S		29 T	A	G		30 D	31 O	W	N
32 N	Y		33 W	H	Y		34 T	O	W	E	D
		35 S	36 T	A	R		37 S	H	O	E
38 L	O	R	D	O	F	39 L	O	R	D	40 S
41 H	I	R	E		42 N	A	U	M		43 H	U	44 T
45 A	N	T	E		46 E	Z	R	A		47 I	R	E
48 M	E	S	S		49 S	E			50 M	E	N

Puzzle 9

1 M	2 A	3 R		4 C	5 H	6 O	7 P		8 R	9 A	10 R	11 E
12 E	R	E		13 H	A	R	E		14 E	R	I	E
15 T	E	D		16 O	R	E	N		17 M	E	D	E
	18 E	19 A	S	T		20 N	21 O	I	S	E	S
22 T	23 H	E	M	E		24 P	I	N	T
25 W	O	M	E	N		26 L	E	E		27 F	28 E	29 D
30 O	M	E	N		31 H	A	S		32 R	A	L	E
33 S	E	R		34 D	E	N		35 F	A	L	S	E
	36 M	O	A	T		37 E	N	T	E	R
38 R	39 E	P	E	N	T		41 R	A	T	E
42 E	V	E	R		43 H	44 O	U	R		45 R	46 E	47 D
48 N	E	A	R		49 E	L	S	E		50 E	R	R
51 O	N	L	Y		52 N	E	E	D		53 D	A	Y

Puzzle 10

	1 N	2 A	3 I	4 L	5 S		6 B	7 R	8 E	9 E	10 D
11 L	E	A	V	E	N		12 R	E	N	T	E	13 D
14 E	A	R		15 S	A	16 R	A	I		17 A	L	E
18 A	R			19 T	R	A	I	N		20 U	B
21 V	E	22 I	23 L		24 E	N	D		25 M	26 L	X	I
27 E	R	R	O	R	S		28 S	29 L	30 A	Y	E	R
		31 O	A	T				32 A	R	D
33 B	34 A	N	D	E	D	35 L	Y	S	I	37 A	38 S
39 L	E	S	S		40 E	41 R	A		42 H	A	L	T
43 E	N			44 D	A	I	45 S	Y		46 I	A
47 S	E	48 A		49 A	L	P	H	A		50 P	E	N
51 S	A	D	52 D	L	E		53 E	R	54 R	A	N	D
	55 S	E	V	E	R		56 S	N	I	T	S

Puzzle 11

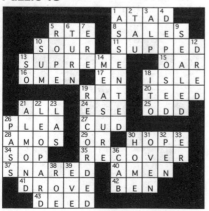

A	R	E		R	I	S	E	S	H	A	S
M	A	D		U	R	K	E	L	A	B	E
E	T		A	S	S	Y	R	I	A	B	E
N	E	E	D	S			V	I	S	E	D
	P	O	E	T		H	E	L	P		
E	L	I		T	R	U	E	R	I	D	A
T	I	S		A	S	A		R	O	W	
A	P	T		S	M	A	R	T	I	C	E
L	A	M	P		D	E	B	T			
T	H	E	R	E		R	E	S	I	N	
R	E		T	A	R	R	I	E	D	S	O
O	R	E		R	A	I	L	S	A	L	A
W	E	N		S	T	A	L	E	N	E	H

Puzzle 12

D	A	W	N		A	E	R	R	O	P	E
A	R	I	A		B	E	E	E	D	E	N
N	E	S	T		I	L	L	C	O	R	E
	S	H	I	E	D		A	L	A	R	M
		O	N	E		T	E	N			
A	T	O	N	E	S		E	A	T	I	N	G
W	O	N						N	E	O	
L	O	O	S	E	D		B	A	S	K	E	T
	T	O	E		U	S	E				
M	O	R	N	S		R	A	L	E	D	
M	O	P	E		I	N	N	L	A	I	R
A	L	E	E		R	O	E	E	S	A	U
P	E	N	T		E	N	D	R	E	L	S

Puzzle 13

S	A	M		G	E	T	S	R	I	D	E
A	G	E		L	A	I	C	E	N	O	N
F	A	T	H	E	R		A	B	A	S	E	D
E	R	R	E	D		R	A	C	E		
	I	T	E	M	S		S	H	R	E	W
S	U	C	H		E	T	A	T	T	E	E
T	N		B	L	A	M	E		R	N	
A	D	E		E	T	R	E	B	O		S
R	O	U	S	E		E	N	D	O	R	
	N	E	R	I		E	R	A	S	E	
S	P	I	R	I	T		D	A	N	C	E	S
E	N	C	E		C	A	I	N	L	E	A
T		E	D		H	I	S	S	E	M	U

Puzzle 14

E	R	S		T	A	S	K	S	M	A	D
S	A	P		A	L	E	P	H	A	D	O
S	W	A	L	L	O	W		E	A	T	E	N
	R	I	O	T		S	A	L	T		
C	A	R	O	N		S	E	R	P	E	N	T
A	N	O	N		H	A	R	E	S	O	R
L	O	W		C	O	V	E	R	A	B	E
E	D		S	A	V	E		A	B	L	E
B	E	E	T	L	E	S		C	R	I	E	S
		N	E	L	L		R	O	A	D	
T	H	E	M	E		N	U	M	B	E	R	S
I	A	M		S	H	E	E	P	T	I	E
S	T	Y		T	O	A	D	S	H	O	T

Puzzle 15

								A	T	A	D
		R	T	E		S	A	L	E	S	
	S	O	U	R		S	U	P	P	E	D
S	U	P	R	E	M	E		O	A	R	
O	M	E	N		E	N		I	S	L	E
		R	A	T		T	E	E	D		
A	L	L		E	S	E		O	D	D	
P	L	E	A		C	U	D				
A	M	O	S		O	R		H	O	P	E
S	O	P		R	E	C	O	V	E	R	
S	N	A	R	E	D		A	M	E	N	
D	R	O	V	E		B	E	N			
	D	E	E	D							

Puzzle 16

R	O	B		H	A	L	F	O	H	M
E	N	O	S		O	L	E	O	B	O	A
A	C	R	E		E	T	E	R	N	I	T	Y
L	E	N	T			M	I				
	A	S	I	D	E		S	L	A	V	E
L	E	G		C	E	L	L		G	E	L
A	S	A		E	N	D	E	D	R	I	M
H	A	I		T	E	A	R	E	L	S
R	U	N	N	Y		R	H	Y	M	E
		O	E	D			O	M	E	R
S	T	E	W	A	R	D	S	S	E	M	I
E	E	R		R	A	I	L	S	N	I	P
E	Y	E		S	W	A	Y	T	R	E

Puzzle 17

		C	A	V	E		F	L	O	W	
	B	A	T	O	N		L	I	G	H	T
S	I	N	E	W		S	U	P		Y	E	T
A	S	E			N	U	T	S			N	O
L	O			C	A	S	E		S	T	O	P
E	N	D		A	M	A		L	I	O	N	S
		R	A	G	E		N	O	N	E		
S	H	A	R	E		D	E	N		S	E	W
H	U	G	E		P	A	T	E			M	E
O	N			S	I	R	S		S	T	I	R
E	T	E		H	E	N		S	H	A	M	E
	S	A	D	O	C		H	A	U	L	S	
	R	O	D	E		T	Y	R	E			

Puzzle 18

GILD HELP STE
AREA PLEA PEA
PEARL MER LAT
KID STAIRS
SLEEPER NET
TORN TAMER HO
USE SENOR MAN
BE BARGE LATE
CAN ESCAPES
BRANDS AW
EAR ALL LYDIA
ARE LAIR EONS
RED SPIN RENE

Puzzle 19

ANGE ADAM ARM
ROLL PARA COO
TROD EMIR REO
READS CHEST
THIRD SHE
RIO SEAT AMOS
ELUL DYE LIVE
ELSE GEMS NEE
ATE THINK
SHAPE FLEES
OER ARIA ATAD
RAM COST REBA
TRY HOTE TRIG

Puzzle 20

BEL SHEBA DAY
APE PANEL RIE
SINNERS MAIDS
TINE LOVE
SPILT VENISON
MULE BINDS MA
ELS LANDS HEM
AS SORES SAGE
REDUCES PAPAS
ONUS HELP
LEEKS MENTION
ANS TRAIN ERE
GET SORRY RED

Puzzle 21

PSALMS THARA
RESIDES RAGES
ALT SAT IRONS
MAIL LOVED DE
SHREW RID TEN
NAMES DIRT
PEDRO IDOLS
ERES UNTIE
SEL PRE ASHER
HP MANSE TALE
KAMEL TAR IDE
ORATE STIRRED
LEPER SATYRS

Puzzle 22

LAMB ABEL TEA
AREA RAVE RAW
WEAK TREASURE
SETS SPEND
CRUDE BETA
AIR ATAD SPAT
ICE RARER RUE
NEST LANA END
INC TESTS
OPHNI BEDS
PLEASURE GULF
EER ASIA ERIE
NAB NEAR DEED

Puzzle 23

T	S	P	A	L	O	N	E	S	P	A
O	I	L	S	O	P	E	N	H	A	S
S	T	O	L	E	T	A	S	T	E	T	H
	W	A	R		T	I	E	R	S	
T	R	I	V	I	A	L	G	A	D	
R	E	N	E	L	I	O	N	S	A	T
E	N	G	A	M	A	S	S	O	D	E
E	T	C	H	A	R	T	A	N	O	N
A	H	A	S	E	A	L	E	S	T	
G	R	A	Z	E	O	M	I	T		
M	O	O	R	I	N	G	T	A	H	O	E
E	R	S	A	V	E	R	S	A	R	I
N	E	E	H	Y	E	N	A	T	A	N

Puzzle 24

J	A	Y	A	S	P	H	E	M		
O	W	E	N	E	T	E	N	O	S	
Y	E	L	L	O	W	D	I	D	H	A
P	I	N	M	A	R	S	O	S	
L	A	S	T	M	A	N	B	A	T	H
O	G	B	E	D	P	E	N	
G	O	L	D	E	N	D	I	G	G	E	D
E	Y	E	H	O	T	A	R	
D	I	N	E	W	A	G	D	U	T	Y
A	R	T	T	A	P	S	I	P
M	A	F	I	R	T	E	M	P	E	R
M	E	A	N	B	E	N	E	L	F
D	R	Y	E	N	D	R	I	D

Puzzle 25

F	I	R	L	A	M	P	L	E	S	S
A	C	E	I	D	O	L	I	R	O	N
R	E	M	O	V	E	A	R	E	L	O
A	W	E	A	N	T	D	E	W
R	A	I	L	A	P	T	E	A	S	Y
U	R	N	S	I	P	C	A	Y
N	M	T	E	L	L	E	S	T	H	O
L	O	W	I	R	A	F	E	W
S	H	O	E	S	E	E	L	A	M	E
H	I	T	S	A	D	W	E	T
A	R	A	R	K	M	I	G	H	T	Y
D	E	A	R	E	D	E	N	E	W	E
E	D	I	T	S	O	N	G	R	O	T

Puzzle 26

M	I	S	S	B	E	A	R	E	R	E
A	R	C	H	E	L	S	E	R	O	W
A	S	H	E	R	P	L	E	A	S	E
O	R	E	O	E	A	S	E	S
P	R	O	D	U	C	T	A	R	E
O	I	L	C	R	O	S	S	L	B
L	O	G	U	I	L	E	A	I
E	T	C	A	R	E	D	A	T	E
H	U	R	D	E	L	I	V	E	R
S	T	O	R	M	R	I	S	E
A	S	L	E	E	P	T	A	R	A	H
G	A	D	N	A	M	E	A	S	I	A
E	R	S	T	W	I	N	C	E	L	T

Puzzle 27

O	W	L	S	S	L	A	P	
T	R	I	A	L	T	A	M	E	D
G	R	A	N	D	E	A	D	O	R	A	M
O	A	T	D	E	N	Y	S	I	N	E
A	L	O	E	P	A	I	R	S	C	I
L	A	R	G	E	G	N	A	S	H	E	R
G	A	P	G	I	N
B	L	E	S	S	E	S	N	O	B	L	E
L	U	R	T	O	U	R	W	E	E	D
E	T	R	E	P	R	A	Y	E	V	E
W	E	A	S	E	L	H	E	A	V	E	N
S	N	A	K	E	A	L	T	E	R
D	U	E	S	B	L	T	S

Puzzle 28

S	I	R	S	A	C	R	E	O	W	L
P	O	E	T	R	O	A	D	P	O	E
A	N	N	A	E	M	S	N	E	E	D
E	G	G	B	E	G	I	N
S	W	E	A	R	D	O	T	A	S
C	L	I	D	A	M	D	R	O	V	E
L	I	N	E	M	A	D	E	V	E	R
A	N	G	R	Y	R	U	E	E	R	E
P	G	R	E	D	E	N	T	R	Y
B	O	A	R	D	S	E	C
S	E	E	R	E	A	T	R	O	B	E
A	W	L	B	A	R	E	A	M	O	S
Y	E	T	E	D	E	N	H	E	A	T

Puzzle 29

```
T A M A . R O M E . W A R
E L A M . A N E M . E L I
N A . E D G E . . R E A P
. . T R U E . S T Y . B E
P R I C E . T H I E F . .
L A T E . S H A M . O D D
A S H . S P A R E . R O E
N E E . T I N E . A G U E
. . S T I C K . S W O R D
S H . A R E . M E A T . .
T O W N . . L E A K . E R
O A R . A R I A . E A S E
P R Y . M E E T . N E E D
```

Puzzle 30

```
J A W . P A R E . A I L S
A B E . E B O N . S N E E
W E A K E N E D . S C A R
S T R I P E . O I L . .
. . T E R . A R R O W S
D I N E D . A R E . S E E
A R E S . O L D . C E R T
T O I . A W L . R I D E S
E N G A G E . B E T . .
. H I E . . A M E R C E
R I B S . F O R E S H I P
I D O L . O D E D . E T E
D A R E . E D D Y . A Y E
```

Puzzle 31

```
B A R . A S H E R . A S A
A R T . S T A T E . D E L
B E . F L E S H L Y . E A
E A G L E . . I R O N S .
. E Y E S . N E S T . . .
D A N . P L E A D . H E M
A R E . A R M . . N O E
M A R . T I R E S . I N N
. A N O N . S I D E . .
B A L A K . R O L L S . .
A M . P E O P L E S . A A
T O W . N I S A N . P I N
S K Y . S L I P S . A R K
```

Puzzle 32

```
S A L E . C A R E . T O W
A M O S . A M E N . E W E
P I . T E N T . . B E E S
. . P A R E . P S I . S T
C R E T E . S A I T H . .
R A R E . T H I N . A H A
I C I . T H A N K . P A N
B E L . O I L S . S P I T
. S H O R T . S E E R S
O H . O L D . B E E N . .
M E A T . . M E E T . A I
E R R . O P E N . H E I R
R O E . W O N T . E A R S
```

Puzzle 33

```
S T A R . T R Y . S E M I
E A S E . H O E . L A I R
A R I A . E A T . A C R E
S E A S O N S . A C H E .
. . O W . T A S K . . .
S T O N E . H A . D E W
O W N S . . S U R E
D O E . B E . . S T E A D
. D E N S . U R . .
L E O N . T R E A D E D
W A G E . A R E . N O N O
E T A S . N I L . G O O N
B E L T . S P Y . E R N E
```

Puzzle 34

```
M A R A . F O A M . D O A
O R E B . I D L E . R U B
W A S H . L O A D . E S E
. . T O W E R . E M I T S
S H O R E . . U S A . .
A I R . B E E N . H A L F
I D E A . L A D . I D O L
L E S S . S T O P . O N E
. . E W E . . R O P E D
S H A R E . W H E A T . .
T A X . A S I A . T I R E
A R E . R E S T . H O U R
Y E S . S A T E . S N E E
```

Puzzle 35

E	W	E	S			I	L	L			C	H	E	W
H	I	N	T			N	O	A			O	A	T	H
U	N	D	O			H	U	N			A	R	E	A
D	E	S	I	R	E		C	H	R	I	S	T		
			C	A	R			E	S	S				
W	O	R	S	H	I	P		T	E	N	T	S		
E	V	E		T	I	P			A	I	U			
T	A	U	N	T		T	R	A	M	P	L	E		
		E	A	R		A	R	E						
S	T	A	T	U	E		I	M	A	G	E	S		
W	I	S	H		A	S	S		D	I	V	E		
A	L	E	E		L	I	E		O	V	E	N		
N	E	A	R		M	R	S		W	E	N	T		

Puzzle 36

A	S	P		K	I	N	G			H	O	N	E
P	U	R		E	S	A	U			O	S	E	E
T	E	E		D	A	Y	S			W	H	E	N
		S	T	A	R		D	E	E	D			
S	P	E	A	R		R	H	O		A			
P	A	N	T		B	E	A	S	T		C	A	
A	R	T		H	E	A	R	T		S	O	N	
N	T		H	E	N	C	E		W	I	L	T	
		F	O	R	T	H		H	A	L	T	S	
	T	R	U	E			F	I	R	E			
H	I	E	S		T	E	A	R		N	N	E	
A	L	E	E		R	A	M	A		C	O	E	
M	E	S	S		I	T	E	M		E	R	E	

Puzzle 37

M	T	S		B	A	L	M		A	H	A	B
I	R	A		E	R	I	E		B	A	D	E
S	E	T	S		A	S	S		I	R	O	N
T	E	E	T	H		A	S	I	D	E		
		R	E	S		E	N	E		D	O	
A	N	O	I	N	T	I	N	G		T	I	N
R	E	A	P		E	R	G		S	O	R	E
M	A	R		W	A	T	E	R	P	O	T	S
S	R		G	O	D		R	O	E			
		T	H	E	F	T		D	A	N	C	E
A	H	I	O		A	R	E		R	E	A	D
H	U	M	S		S	U	R	E		R	I	E
A	B	E	T		T	E	A	R		I	N	N

Puzzle 38

W	A	R	S		K	E	E	P		C	A	B
E	S	E	K		A	L	A	S		H	U	E
B	A	S	I	N	S		T	A	L	E	N	T
		U	R	I	M		L	I	E	T	H	
H	A	L	T	S		D	O	M	E	S		
A	C	T		A	N	O	N		S	E	L	L
I	N		N	A	V	E	S		I	E		
L	E	S	S		P	E	S	T		M	E	N
		P	O	W	E	R		A	M	E	N	D
S	H	O	N	E			A	L	A	N		
L	O	O	S	E	D		S	E	N	S	E	S
I	N	N		P	I	C	K		N	E	S	T
T	E	S		S	E	A	S		A	S	P	S

Puzzle 39

S	C	A	L	P	S		S	A	V	E	D
H	A	S	T	I	L	Y		E	X	I	L	E
A	M	I		T	E	E		V	I	N	E	S
N	E	E	T		W	A	G	E	S		M	I
A	L	L	O	T		R	U	N		M	E	R
		L	O	O	S	E		M	A	N	E	
	P	I	L	O	T		S	H	O	R	T	
M	I	L	S		H	A	T	E	S			
A	T	L		G	E	L		M	E	T	E	D
D	C		D	A	R	T	S		S	A	V	E
E	H		O	R		E	E	E		B	E	E
S	E	I	N	E		R	E	S	P	O	N	D
T	R	E	E	S		S	P	O	R	T	S	

Puzzle 40

H	A	L	E		L	E	A	P
S	E	V	E	N		E	A	G	L	E
T	H	R	E	A	T		T	R	U	E	S	T
R	A	M		K	E	P	T		R	A	T	E
A	M	O	S		R	E	E	L		S	E	E
P	E	N	N	S		P	R	E	F	E	R	S
		O	P	P		S	A	L				
F	R	O	W	A	R	D		F	A	D	E	S
O	I	L		S	A	U	L		T	I	D	E
E	V	I	L		Y	E	A	R		A	G	E
S	E	V	E	R	E		M	I	N	D	E	D
	S	E	V	E	R		B	O	N	E	S	
	S	I	T	S		S	T	E	M			

Puzzle 41

```
M A P   S W A M   S M E E
A B I   T A R E   H E A R
R E S T O R E D   E A R N
S T A I N   S E A T S
    T E A   S H U N S
A R C H   S I G H   R A E
P U R E   I L O   R E V E
E T E   H A L L   E D E N
S H A D E   D I A
    T E N T H   S L O P E
E R I E   R E M E M B E R
L O O P   O R A   E P I
M E N S   W A R T   D E E
```

Puzzle 42

```
I R E   S H I P   I D O L
T E L   C A L M   M I R E
E L I   A L L   S P E E D
      H A T E   S R A
I R U S T   G L O R I F Y
I E   A E R I E   T A R E
R A E   R I V E R   M A A
A C R E   P E T E R   M R
S H R I N E S   S E V E N
        T E N   A T M
W I G H T   P L O   F E W
E R I E   R E A R   E R E
B I E R   R A S E   D A N
```

Puzzle 43

```
  A X L E   O A T S
  A B I E L   T R A I N
A R R I V E   H E R M O N
A D O   C A N   E T A
R E A   A T R I A   O E R
E N D O W   D E M A N D S
    H A Y   L E D
S T R O K E S   N O T C H
E S E   E A S E D   E H I
R A M   R E S   M E N
A R I S E N   S O P P E D
  S T O R E   E N T E R
  S U E D   N E A R
```

Puzzle 44

```
B A D   B R I D E   B A R
E P I   R E M I T   I C E
D E F I E D   M E N D E D
    F R E D S   R O D
T R E A D   T E N D E T H
H U R T   R I T A   N O E
U L   E M E R A L D   W A
M E T   E A R S   R A I L
B R A I L L E   P O S T S
    S A T   D R A W S
N U T M E G   O R N E R Y
O R E   T E M P T   N Y E
B E D   H O L E S   T E A
```

Puzzle 45

```
R A M   B E N   S O N
A D O   E N E   P A U L
W A S T E D   H U R   A H
  E O N   H E N   S T E
W A S P   L O W   S T E M
A S   S I T   P E A
S P R E A D   N E A R L Y
  O A T   D O N   I E
C O L T   F A T   P L E A
A W L   L A Y   F O E
B E   A I R   P L E A S E
  D E C K   V I A   R U N
  A T E   A N T   N E E
```

Puzzle 46

```
A M A N A     K I T E S
R E F I N E   S N E E Z E
M E T   N L   H I   E R A
S T   D U S T O F F   A L
    B E L I E V E R S
B A R S   E N E   O H I O
E X I T         W I D E
D E E R   G T O   A P E R
    F O L L O W E R S
E R   Y E A R N E D   G P
R E O   A N   E R   B I O
R E W A R D   R I V E R S
S K E I N     E A G L E
```

Puzzle 47

O	E	R		R	A	N	G	E		P	A	N
A	R	E		I	D	O	L	S		R	I	A
F	R	I	E	N	D		E	A	S	I	L	Y
		G	A	G		T	A	U	P	E		
L	E	N	T		D	I	M		I	S	L	E
E	N	S		S	I	N		E	N	T	E	R
A	D		S	I	N	G	E	R	S		P	G
V	O	W	E	D		L	A		R	E		
E	W	E	R		V	E	T		H	E	R	D
	A	V	O	I	D		S	A	D			
B	A	K	E	R	S		S	I	L	E	N	T
O	W	E		E	I	G	H	T		E	O	N
W	E	N		T	O	Y	S		M	E	T	

Puzzle 48

S	E	A	S		A	B	D	A		A	R	E
I	T	C	H		N	A	I	L		M	E	R
R	A	C	E		T	R	A	P		E	A	R
		E	E	R	I	E		H	A	N	D	S
H	A	P	P	Y		T	A	B				
E	S	T		E	A	S	E		B	A	N	D
L	I	E	S		G	I	N		A	L	O	E
L	A	D	E		U	N	D	O		T	O	E
	E	R	E			A	M	E	N	D		
C	H	I	D	E		E	R	R	O	R		
H	I	D		S	I	D	E		L	E	V	I
O	R	E		T	R	E	E		E	T	A	L
P	E	A		S	E	N	D		S	H	U	L

Puzzle 49

T	I	M	E		P	U	R		C	E	N	T
A	N	O	N		A	T	E		O	S	A	Y
U	N	B	E	L	I	E	F		P	A	I	R
		R	I	D		I	M	P	U	R	E	
B	A	R	G	E		A	L	E	E			
O	B	E	Y		E	N	L	A	R	G	E	D
R	E	S		A	N	G	E	L		O	D	E
A	T	T	E	N	D	E	D		A	R	E	A
		A	D	E	S		S	P	E	N	D	
P	E	R	S	I	A		A	S	P			
S	L	I	T		V	I	G	I	L	A	N	T
I	S	L	E		O	R	E		E	V	E	S
S	E	E	R		R	E	D		S	A	T	E

Puzzle 50

E	L	I		J	E	S	U	S		R	A	P
W	E	N		A	V	I	T	H		I	C	E
E	A		O	M	E	N		O	R	D	E	R
S	H	A	P	E	N		R	U	E			
		M	E	S		R	E	T	I	R	E	D
A	N	O	N		L	I	N	E	N		A	R
B	E	N		F	A	V	O	R		U	S	E
E	R		T	A	K	E	N		B	L	E	W
L	I	G	H	T	E	R		M	I	L		
		H	I	N			R	E	T	A	I	N
S	T	O	N	E		L	A	D	E		R	E
T	E	S		S	H	I	N	E		M	O	S
P	A	T		S	E	E	K	S		A	N	T